READINGS IN

AUTOMATIC LANGUAGE PROCESSING

EDITED BY

DAVID G. HAYS

The RAND Corporation

NEW YORK

AMERICAN ELSEVIER PUBLISHING COMPANY INC.

1966

SOLE DISTRIBUTORS FOR GREAT BRITAIN
ELSEVIER PUBLISHING COMPANY, LTD
Barking, Essex, England

SOLE DISTRIBUTORS FOR THE CONTINENT OF EUROPE
ELSEVIER PUBLISHING COMPANY
Amsterdam, The Netherlands

Library of Congress Catalog Card Number: 66-19743

Table of Contents

iii

Preface

The readings collected in this volume are not intended to substitute for a textbook, but to supplement one. In a university course, with a series of lectures to provide the central framework and a few longer monographic publications to treat key areas in greater detail, this volume might suffice, but that is not its proper role.

It is not intended to introduce a novice to the digital computer, for he can acquire a better introduction in many ways; the elementary statements in the following introduction may lead some readers to go in search of a proper description of the computer and how it is programmed, but that is another matter. A previous acquaintance with linguistics is also advisable.

The papers presented here are not always the historically significant contributions, but if I had taken a historian's view I could not have abridged the individual readings as I did.

I have included these papers because they epitomize, in their various ways, methods, solutions to central problems, or approaches to the use of the computer as a processor of natural language. Other papers will undoubtedly refine, or perhaps supersede, the concepts that the reader can learn from these pages. But I have tried to choose papers in which sound concepts were developed with enough richness of detail to let the reader see how it all works.

I am grateful to the authors who permitted me to reprint their work, and to abridge in order to conserve space. I am likewise grateful to the publishers whose permission to reprint I hereby acknowledge. And I apologize to the authors of equally meritorious papers for which I was not able to find a place. I trust that the reader, after this introduction to the field, will be prepared to seek them out.

D.G.H.

1 Introduction

This book takes the name of a field that encompasses every use to which computers can be put in the manipulation of ordinary language—the kind of language spoken and written every day by almost every human being in the course of his private, commercial, or academic routine. The papers in this book do not cover the whole breadth of what computational linguistics will one day span. It would not be possible, as computational linguistics is entering its second decade and the digital computer its third, to predict every application to which linguists will put the computer in the future nor the kind of programs that will make the computer an entirely useful tool for the jobs that have already been invented for it. By 1945 it was obvious to a few engineers and mathematicians that automatic machines could be constructed to perform any numerical calculation; by 1955, a few linguists had realized that the advancement of their science required the computer, and that by means of their knowledge the computer could be put to work in new, useful areas. Perhaps by 1975 applied computational linguistics will be known to everyman, and it will be possible to estimate the true market for automatic language processing. In 1965, university scholars are just beginning to adopt the computer as a research tool, and commercial applications are just beginning to show a profit.

The importance of the automatic digital computer as a laboratory instrument is known to everyone. It serves two major purposes: reduction of data and derivation of conclusions from theoretical premises. Like physics, with its voluminous collections of cloud-chamber photographs and like sociology, with its massive collection of census reports and other demographic data and like biochemistry, with tens of thousands of compounds to test for possibly beneficent physiological activity, linguistics has more data than any previous generation of linguists knew what to do with. Every published book, newspaper, and magazine is a sample of human use of language, and if he prefers to observe language in its spoken rather than its written form, the linguist has only to turn on a tape recorder beside his radio or television set or wherever a conversation takes place. But it does no good to record these data if analysis is impossible. The human scholar can hope to identify only a few of the patterns, regularities, and systematic features that could be found by fully detailed, uniformly thorough analysis of every available specimen of human language. Insofar as the computer

1

can be programmed to inspect the material at hand, and to report what it finds in summary terms, it becomes the linguist's indispensable assistant.

A theory is a collection of fundamental propositions about reality. Taken together, these propositions predict many—often indefinitely many—consequences, sometimes testable and sometimes not. The task of the theoretician is to discover what these consequences are, and it is exceedingly hard work. Computers are often used as working models of theoretical systems; they are allowed to operate randomly, except for the constraints imposed by the theoretical principle being tested, so that the results of their calculations can be ascribed in part to chance, in part to the theory being tested. This technique, first called the Monte Carlo method and now often described as simulation, has given the computer a second major role in science. The intricate phenomena called natural language can be described only by theories of great complexity; computer simulation is being used to test the consistency of linguistic theories and to help isolate the weak points where they require strengthening.

Outside the field of linguistics, and therefore to be counted among applications, several branches of social science need the digital computer in its guise of language processor as a laboratory tool. Psychology, sociology, and anthropology are largely—if not altogether—dependent on the analysis of what the persons studied say and write. Social scientists conduct interviews, observe group discussions, collect letters, diaries, and other private communications, examine the contents of newspapers and other mass media, and so on. Whereas the linguist's interest is in the form of expression, the social scientist's concern is with content, and a special kind of content at that: the internal state that causes a person to utter a particular sentence, in a particular context, at a particular time, and the effect on his audience of what he says. To take the case of group discussions, how can affection, respect, and authority be predicted from what the discussants have said to one another in the course of a few hours of conversation? Or to take an example from history, how can the motivations of a leading personality be estimated from his memoirs, notes, and other papers of a certain period? A computer program based exclusively on the linguist's theory of language could not be expected to serve the social scientist's purposes, yet one might expect that analysis of forms of expression would be, in each application, prerequisite to the analysis of content, and so it has turned out.

The library is the scene of another exceedingly obvious application of computational linguistics. Knowledge is preserved from generation to generation in many forms, in sound recordings, motion pictures, charts and diagrams, models, and many other guises; yet text remains the predominant medium for the preservation of what the earlier generations have learned. Until writing was invented, the upper limit on what a culture could remember of its own past was narrowly limited; everything had to be remembered, and even with specialists in the art of memorization no culture was ever able to preserve a small fraction of what the earliest collections of manuscript brought together. Libraries have been growing for two millenia, and they seem to be reaching a new kind of limit: the upper limit of what can be preserved by a culture without active mechanisms for locating what is stored. Subject classifications and indexes, implemented with card catalogues and similar systems, are scarcely adequate for libraries of twenty million volumes, and the world's most important research libraries are now passing that mark. The computer has been called on to provide a solution to this problem; like the social scientist, the librarian is concerned with the content of text, not with the form. An article in a scientific journal is intended as a contribution to knowledge; the librarian's task is to discover where, in the vast, indefinitely complex body of facts comprising man's knowledge of himself and his universe this contribution fits. What does it repeat in order to demonstrate its proper position, what does it contribute that is novel, what new connections does it make among known facts? Perhaps no librarian has ever made such an analysis of a library, but librarians with computers programmed for automatic language processing may eventually be able to do just that. Such at least is the goal of automatic documentation.

Other important and difficult areas of application for computational linguistics have been noted. Machine translation was probably the first. Here the goal is to translate the content of a document or spoken message from one spoken language into another. Programming digital computers, even when the purpose of the program is simple numerical processing, is to some degree applied computational linguistics. The languages used by the earliest programmers were exceedingly simple, not calling for the same kind of theoretical models for their analysis as do the natural languages. As programmers attempt to do more and more difficult tasks, they require more and more powerful languages. Furthermore, they are attempting to relinquish their original duties to less well-trained users. If a person without detailed training in the design of computer programs is to explain directly to the computer what he wants done in more and more difficult cases, computers must be provided with programs for language processing in order to translate the user's statement into a sequence of operations.

Thus one branch of computer programming has moved very close to linguistics. Other applications of automatic language processing in business and government come to mind as soon as one observes the obvious fact that buyers and sellers, administrators and underlings, like all the rest of humanity, exchange enormous quantities of words every day. To help them in processing their correspondence would be profitable. The applications in teaching could be equally important. Finally, there is a range of applications that calls for much less sophisticated knowledge of natural language, but that has already demonstrated how major changes in industry can be brought about with simple ideas. Typists and typesetters occupy themselves for millions of hours each year with the remaking of text: copying from one sheet onto another, producing "clean copy" by collating corrections, deletions, format instructions, and hyphenation with "a preliminary draft." If the preliminary draft is stored in the memory of a digital computer, the collation can be made automatic. The typist need only transcribe the amendments, leaving the computer to carry forward what was correct on the draft, to put the changes in at the right places, to arrange the format as it ought to be, and to justify lines if that is called for. Many newspapers are now produced in this manner, books are printed with the help of computers, and it seems obvious that in time virtually every typewriter operated by a paid employee will be connected in some manner to a computer. And here the circle closes, for the text put into the computer for the sake of reducing cost and increasing speed in the publication industry becomes a base on which the linguist can perform his research.

Pure computational linguistics and its several applications are unified by their common employment of certain techniques and processes that make up the specific substance of the field. Linguistics as a whole, and abstract linguistic theories, are not directly concerned with the computer. Algorithms appropriate for carrying out the processes suggested by linguistic theory and the facts of natural language are a special problem, one with which the linguist need not concern himself unless he chooses. The computer can aid him, whether he understands its workings or not. Nevertheless, tradition has it that the good craftsman knows his tools and, therefore, every linguist has good reason to choose to know at least a little about the computer.

In comparison with empirical procedures, computer-based methods for handling large files of text, large dictionaries, complicated grammars, and other large files of data are fantastically easy. Still, these files have to be prepared for input to the computer, arranged conveniently in the computer's active storage area, transferred to and from inexpensive media for permanent retention, reorganized, and printed out for inspection. In short, one group of elementary processes required throughout computational linguistics constitutes a system for file maintenance. Textual and similar materials generally go into the computer by way of a keyboard operation. There are typewriters that produce paper tape, punched cards, and magnetic tape; they are manufactured with many different character sets, some very limited and others satisfyingly large. It is also possible to connect one or many typewriters directly to a computer, through electrical wiring. The operating speeds of contemporary computers are so high that a computer can recognize each key stroke as it occurs on each of a hundred typewriters being operated simultaneously by fast typists and still have time between strokes to carry out some simple computations.

Inside the computer, the usual storage medium is an array of magnetic cores, each holding just one bit of information; six or eight bits are commonly used to represent a character. Standard large computers can retain about two hundred thousand characters in storage. Magnetic tape, on which information is recorded in the same way that sound is recorded by home tape recorders, is the usual medium for inexpensive storage. Information can be transferred automatically at high rates between machine storage and tape.

The computer is also equipped with its own printing devices, operating at high speed, with fonts of from 48 to about 250 characters. Type can be set automatically from tapes produced by computers; although this process is slower and more expensive than direct computer printout, it provides for an exceedingly wide variety of characters and very high quality.

The most elementary operations of input, internal arrangement, and output are provided for either in the equipment as constructed or in programs furnished for general use. The linguist working with computers does not have to begin by designing typewriters or working out convenient ways of moving large volumes of information to and from magnetic tape. The lowest level that he has to control for himself is the encoding of his large character set and the features of arrangement on the printed page that he wishes to preserve. A six-bit machine character corresponds to one of sixty-four possibilities; in publishing a book, a typographer can call for characters from a set of several hundred or several thousand. One of the typographer's characters must therefore be represented, in some manner, by several machine characters. This is the problem of text encoding. A good scheme retains all the useful information of the printed book and makes it easy to isolate those aspects of the information about a character that are needed, for example, in alphabetization.

The linguist's files are organized in various ways, from a linguistic point of view, and their organization must be represented within the computer. Text is organized into articles, books, subject collections, and so on. Dictionaries are organized into entries, each with various parts: heading, grammatical description, definition, and so on. A grammar, a bibliography, a concordance, an index verborum, a thesaurus, a computer program—each kind of file has a definite pattern of organization. After the content of the file is first prepared and put into the computer, it is often necessary to add further information, either for a new element—as when new words are added to a dictionary—or of new kinds. Files from different sources, but of the same kind, sometimes have to be merged; thus, two dictionaries of the same language might be assembled into a single, larger dictionary. In merging, provision must be made for putting the elements of the composite file in proper order, detecting and dealing appropriately with overlap, and so on.

Files have to be consulted; in some cases, consultation amounts to looking for one specific item whose place in the file may or may not be known. Thus, if a dictionary is arranged alphabetically by heading, finding the entry for a given word entails only going a certain distance through the alphabet; but if a bibliography is arranged alphabetically by author, and one or more entries on a certain subject are to be found, the subject identification in each entry must be checked.

Sometimes file consultation must be performed on a wholesale basis, which is as much as to say that the content of two files must be compared. For many purposes, the processing of text must begin with dictionary lookup for every word. When the text is small enough to be stored in the high-speed memory of the computer, the dictionary can be read in little by little, and each entry in turn can be compared with all the words in text; when the dictionary is small enough to be stored, the text can be read one word at a time. When both dictionary and text are too large, some process must be found to facilitate all the comparisons; and when both are large enough, the magnitude of the task justifies ingenuity of the highest order.

Syntactic analysis of a text, the determination of sentence structures, can be regarded as another kind of file consultation. Yet it is certainly more complex than dictionary lookup. The units of text that are to be matched with dictionary entries are explicitly, overtly present in the text, ready to be matched. A grammar, when it can be regarded as a list of phrases, consists of phrase descriptions to be matched against text, but the phrases are only implicitly present in the text to begin with. A phrase described in the grammar may consist of two parts, of which one part is potentially itself a phrase. But the constituent phrase has its parts in turn, and only the ultimate constituents are overtly represented in the text after dictionary lookup. Parsing algorithms are devoted to cyclical, or recursive, comparison of text with grammar so that in effect the phrasal construction of the text is made explicit, each phrase appearing in time to be identified as part of a larger phrase.

Grammars are large tables, when they can be treated as tables at all, and unlike dictionaries their entries are interrelated in complex ways. A dictionary can be revised by the simple addition of a new word. When a new kind of phrase is added to a grammar, or when a new distinction among parts of phrases is introduced, many other parts of the grammar can be implicated, and far-reaching alterations may be necessary. How best to organize a grammar for consultation during parsing has been the object of much investigation. Besides tables, computer programs have been suggested as representations of grammar, and systematic accounts of the features that permit constituents to be bound together in phrases have also been recommended.

The inventory of elementary processes out of which programs for automatic language processing can be built is not exhausted by our current knowledge of the structure of language. We are well enough aware of our ignorance to see, dimly, further aspects of language structure, and much of what we can hope to bring within our control during the years ahead is concerned with the representation of meaning. One necessity that seems to face us is the use of further dictionaries. In the first dictionary, a string of letters is associated with grammatical and other properties; in the second dictionary, syntactically connected parts of sentences are tabulated and associated with elements of meaning. Such dictionaries are apparently necessary in information retrieval and all other applications where content, the substance of what is said, must be processed.

No branch of science or technology is ever complete, but books occasionally must be completed so that science and technology may go on. To regret that this volume of readings cannot cover every conceivable branch of its subject would be to deny its readers the hope that by clear thinking and industry they may contribute to further growth. There is room for growth; our ability to process natural language materials automatically, almost nonexistent a decade ago, has reached a level that permits us to look forward to more useful and more intellectually satisfying, and certainly far more complex, elaborations.

2 Specification Languages for Mechanical Languages and their Processors – A Baker's Dozen

Saul Gorn

1. Introduction

Many varieties of mechanical languages and the languages which specify their syntax exist. By many techniques and devices these syntactical languages specify concepts and processes. In these languages it is possible to specify the same object in different ways to obtain clarity from different points of view. The choice of the language depends upon its convenience in specifying or communicating a concept.

The purpose of this paper is to show to what extent the languages illustrated are capable of specifying such mechanical languages or their processors, and to what extent these specifying languages are equivalent in their ease of mechanical translation among themselves.

To dispel some of the confusion as to the power of applicability of these languages, one trivial example is worked over in a dozen different ways. The simplicity of this example provides the link permitting the comparison of the methods of specification. The processor (used by McNaughton as an illustration of logical nets) being specified we will call the *triple sequence alarm*. The corresponding input language of strings of zeros and ones we may call the *triple one sequenced strings*. The processor itself as shown in Fig. 1 may be considered a *data generator* or a *triple one sequenced string recognizer*.

The dozen specifying languages can be given the titles and classifications

---

Note: The material in this paper comes from the University of Pennsylvania's Office of Computer Research and Education and is an outcome of the work jointly supported by the National Science Foundation Grant G-14096 and the Air Force Office of Scientific Research AF-49(638)951. Reprinted with the permission of author and publisher from *Communications of the Association for Computing Machinery*, Vol. 4, No. 12 (December 1961), pp. 532–542.

of Table 1. The groups not separated by double lines are mechanically translatable into one another from top down. Translation between these groups calls for heuristic methods.

The examples will illustrate some of the terminology presented in the

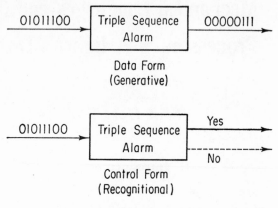

Data Form
(Generative)

Control Form
(Recognitional)

Fig. 1.

author's paper, "Some Basic Terminology Connected with Mechanical Languages and Their Processors" (*Comm. ACM 4* [August 1961], 336). Some of these languages are essentially one-dimensional (linear) and some are essentially two-dimensional (graphic and tabular); some are purely sequential, and some permit simultaneous action; some are more suitable for behavioral (recognitional) specification, and some are better for structural (generative) specification; one is a command language where the others are descriptive; and one is a sublanguage of natural language where the others are mechanical. Finally, some are more suited to specifying languages and some to specifying processors.

For example, one might have a language which is suited to specifying languages structurally but which can be used to specify the *processors* of those languages behaviorally.

2. Natural Language

The "triple sequence alarm" is a device with one input and one output. The input will accept sequences of signals of equal duration chosen from two standard signals which we will designate by the symbols 0 and 1. The output will emit during each of the signal duration intervals one of the two signals, 0 or 1, acceptable by the input. The device is such that a signal 0 will be produced at each signal duration interval until the first occurrence of a signal 1 which had signals 1 as its two immediate predecessors; at

Table 1. Classification of Specifying Languages

Title	Dimension	Timing	Mode	Structural or Behavioral	Processor or Language
1. Natural Language	1?	Sequential or Simultaneous	Descriptive or Command	Structural or Behavioral	Processor or Language
2. Regular Expression	1	Sequential	Descriptive	Structural ——— Behavioral	Language ——— Processor
3. Backus Normal Form	1	Sequential	Descriptive	Structural	Language
4. Trees	2	Sequential	Descriptive	Structural	Language
5. Prefix	1	Sequential	Descriptive	Structural	Language
6. State Diagram	2	Simultaneous	Descriptive	Behavioral or Structural	Processor
7. Symbol State Diagram	2	Simultaneous	Descriptive	Behavioral or Structural	Processor
8. Incidence-Matrix	2	Simultaneous	Descriptive	Behavioral or Structural	Processor
9. Logical Net	2	Simultaneous	Descriptive	Structural	Processor
10. Propositional Logic with Time Variable	1	Simultaneous	Descriptive	Structural	Processor
11. Logical Equations	1	Simultaneous	Mixed	Structural	Processor
12. Turing Machine	1 or 2	Simultaneous	Descriptive	Behavioral or Structural	Processor
13. Flow Chart	2	Sequential or Simultaneous	Mixed or Command	Behavioral or Structural	Processor

that duration interval and for each successive interval until the end of the input string the output signal will be 1.

What we have just given is a descriptive, behavioral specification of the triple sequence alarm processor in a linear sequential sublanguage of a natural language.

3. Regular Expressions

The language-naming language we now present will have, as basic processors, generators and recognizers for a certain class of infinite classes of finite strings of zeros and ones. One such infinite class, for example, is the class of all finite strings of zeros and ones containing somewhere three successive ones, that is, the class of all input strings for which the triple sequence alarm ends with a signal of 1.

The language is that of Kleene's 15 "regular expressions" as modified by McNaughton.16 We now specify the "regular expression language-naming language" in natural language (our next example will present the specification in a mechanical language), but in a generative manner known as a "production system" (see Gorn 7, 8, 9).

The regular expression language is a linear sequential language of strings of characters chosen from the alphabet $\{0, 1, (,), *, \vee\}$. Each string of characters from this alphabet which is a regular expression will be a partial specification of a linear sequential language of strings of characters chosen from the alphabet $\{0, 1\}$; it will be a structural specification when a processor is specified which will generate all these strings. The purely syntactic generative specification of the regular expression language is the following *production system*

SY_a The one-character string, 0, is a regular expression.

SY_b The one-character string, 1, is a regular expression.

SY_c If a string designated by α is a regular expression, then the string composed in left to right order of "(", the characters of α, ")", and "*" is also a regular expression (briefly, if α is a regular expression, then so is "$(\alpha)*$").

SY_d If the strings designated by α and β are regular expressions, then so is the string constructed by taking all the characters from left to right of α and following them immediately on the right by all of the characters from left to right of β (briefly, if α and β are regular expressions, then so is $\alpha\beta$). This basic procedure for all linear sequential languages is called "concatenation".

SY_e If the strings designated by α and β are regular expressions, then so is the string beginning with "(" concatenated on the right by the characters of α, followed on the right by "$\vee$", then concatenated on the right by the characters of β, and ending with the character ")"; or more briefly stated, if α and β are regular expressions, then so is "$(\alpha \vee \beta)$".

Any particular regular expression is generated by "programming" a particular procedure of sequenced steps from the "order code manual" a, b, c, d, e. For example, applying productions a, b, and d, several times each, produces the strings $\alpha_1 = 1$, $\alpha_2 = 0$, $\alpha_3 = 10$, $\alpha_4 = 110$, and $\alpha_5 = 111$; applying e several times produces the strings $\beta_1 = (0 \vee 1)$, $\beta_2 = ((0 \vee 10) \vee 110)$; applying production c several times produces $\delta_1 = ((0 \vee 1))*$ and $\delta_2 = (((0 \vee 10) \vee 110))*$; finally, applying production d several times produces the regular expression

$$\alpha = (((0 \vee 10) \vee 110))*111((0 \vee 1))*$$

The specification of the "semantic content" of regular expressions can parallel the syntactic generative specification as follows

SE_a The regular expression 0 designates the class of "words" or strings over the alphabet $\{0, 1\}$, which class contains the single element 0, that is, 0 designates the unit class of "binary strings", $\{0\}$.

SE_b The regular expression 1 designates the unit class of "binary strings", $\{1\}$.

SE_c The regular expression designated by $(\alpha)*$ designates the class obtained from the class designated by α as follows: if α_1, α_2, α_3, $\cdots$, and so on designate any binary strings belonging to α, then any strings of the form "null", α_1, $\alpha_1\alpha_2$, $\alpha_1\alpha_2\alpha_3$, $\cdots$ belong to $(\alpha)*$.

SE_d The regular expression designated by $\alpha\beta$ designates the class obtained from the two classes designated by α and β by concatenating any "word" belonging to α on the left of any word belonging to β:

$$\alpha\beta = \{\alpha_i\beta_j : \alpha_i \, \varepsilon \, \alpha, \, \beta_j \, \varepsilon \, \beta\},$$

to use the mathematical notation.

SE_e The class of words designated by a regular expression $(\alpha \vee \beta)$ is obtained by taking the union of the classes designated by regular expressions α and β, respectively, that is $\delta \, \varepsilon \, (\alpha \vee \beta)$ if either $\delta \, \varepsilon \, \alpha$ or $\delta \, \varepsilon \, \beta$.

Thus, it is easy to see that the regular expression

$$\alpha = (((0 \vee 10) \vee 110))*111((0 \vee 1))*$$

constructed above denotes the class of strings (the "extent" of the language) comprising the language of strings of zeros and ones mentioned above, that is, the class of all finite strings of zeros and ones containing somewhere three successive ones. The stated regular expression is even more specific in that it marks the first occurrence, reading from left to right, of three successive ones.

It is obvious that the regular expression type of language need not be restricted to languages with binary alphabet, {0, 1}. The languages so specifiable are also called "finite state languages".

4. Backus Normal Form

We now present a mechanical language designed for generative syntactic specification of digital linear sequential mechanical languages. Its use is called "specification by Backus normal form"* because John Backus of IBM introduced it into the report of the international committee on ALGOL 60. [21, 25] We will first specify the language using natural language as the syntax language, and will then illustrate its use by specifying in it both the language of regular expressions and the language of strings for which the triple sequence alarm was a recognizer.

A Backus syntactic specification language is a linear sequential language over an alphabet (infinite) composed of the following symbols

1. "Bracket" symbols "⟨" and "⟩"
2. "Production" symbol ":: ="
3. "Choice" symbol "|"
4. Two alphabets called "names" and "symbols": both of these are often selections of words from a prior alphabet, and can be infinite in number (not in length). If a control processor is provided which will distinguish in any given occurrence the characters within these words from the characters in 1, 2, and 3, then such characters as ⟨,⟩, :, ::, =, :=, ::=, and | may appear within them. Usually this is not the case and the "names" and "symbols" chosen are restricted in format with respect to the occurrence of these characters.

The individual *names* are intended to denote *auxiliary* languages called *syntactic types* of the language being specified; a string of symbols consisting of "⟨" followed on the right by a name and then followed by "⟩" is intended to designate the extent of the name, that is, the set of strings in the specified language of which it is the name—or, put another way, surrounding a name by these brackets is an operation transforming the intent designated by the name to the set of strings forming the corresponding extent. The intent of a language is the set of processors which will operate upon it.

A *symbol* is intended to name itself; in other words, the individual *symbols* are designated strings of characters from the alphabet of the language

---

* Actually, the form is not normal. It has been justly suggested that it be called "Backus-Naur form". Naur introduced the actual notation, Backus the concepts.

being specified, and often are designations *by the objects themselves* of auxiliary languages with only one word, namely that string. The symbol "|" is used to chain together alternative forms, each of which yields composite syntactic types which are auxiliary languages formed by concatenation. Thus a symbol concatenated with a symbol designates another symbol, a bracketed name concatenated with a symbol designates the set of words obtained by concatenating that symbol with each word of the set designated by the name, a bracketed name concatenated with a bracketed name designates the *product set* of all strings designated by one concatenated on the indicated side by all strings designated by the other.

By using a string of the form: *bracketed name* concatenated on the right by " :: =" concatenated on the right by *a composite name* constructed with "|", bracketed names, symbols, and concatenation we obtain in a very compact form a set of production rules for the sublanguage designated by the bracketed name at the extreme left of the string.

For example, the language specified by the regular expression

$$\alpha = (((0 \vee 10) \vee 110))*111((0 \vee 1))*$$

cited in example 2, and given the name *triple one sequenced strings,* could be specified in Backus normal form as follows

T_1 ⟨null string⟩ :: =

T_2 ⟨single character string⟩ :: = 0 | 1

T_3 ⟨elementary excluded string⟩ :: = 0 | 10 | 110

T_4 ⟨general excluded string⟩ :: = ⟨null string⟩ | ⟨general excluded string⟩ ⟨elementary excluded string⟩

T_5 ⟨general string⟩ :: = ⟨null string⟩ | ⟨general string⟩ ⟨single character string⟩

T_6 ⟨triple one sequenced string⟩ :: = ⟨general excluded string⟩ 111 ⟨general string⟩

Note the tacit assumption in T_4 and T_5 that the null string concatenated on either side by a string yields that string. Note also the similarity in form between T_4 and T_5; it will clearly appear whenever a regular expression ending with an asterisk is being specified.

A Backus syntactic specification is a compact and formal specification, in an appropriate language, of a production system. The specification restrictions implicit in Backus normal form place the languages so specified in the class of "Phrase Structure Languages" (see Chomsky; [4, 5] more specifically, they are the "context-free languages").

As another example, a mechanical specification of the regular expression language which we specified in natural language in example 2 is the following

R_1 ⟨regular expression⟩ :: = ⟨elementary expression⟩ | ⟨or expression⟩ | ⟨star expression⟩
R_2 ⟨star expression⟩ :: = (⟨regular expression⟩)*
R_3 ⟨or expression⟩ :: = (⟨regular expression⟩ ∨ ⟨regular expression⟩)
R_4 ⟨elementary expression⟩ :: = ⟨null string⟩ | 0 | 1 | ⟨regular expression⟩ ⟨regular expression⟩

Finally, let us give as much specification as we can of ⟨Backus language⟩ in Backus language; let the two alphabets (decidable languages), ⟨name⟩, and ⟨symbol⟩, be already specified; let, further, the symbols "←" and "I" and the operation of juxtaposition have the meanings we have described above for ":: =," "|," and concatenation; finally, let ":: =" and "|" be two special characters of the symbol alphabet. Then

B_1 ⟨subject⟩ ← ⟨name⟩
B_2 ⟨predicate⟩ ← ⟨name⟩ I ⟨symbol⟩ I ⟨predicate⟩ | ⟨predicate⟩ I ⟨predicate⟩ ⟨predicate⟩
B_3 ⟨Backus language⟩ ← ⟨subject⟩ :: = ⟨predicate⟩ I ⟨subject⟩ :: =

Clearly, there is much more than just the Backus specification in this specification.

5. Trees

Let us now consider a two-dimensional language for syntactic structural specification. Let us call it a language of *rooted trees* or, when no confusion is possible, simply *tree language*. We now change our method of specification to suit the purposes of our main example, the specification of the triple sequence alarm. Instead of specifying the tree language directly, we will specify the relevant sublanguage of the tree language as the end product of the following generative rules of translation from the generating program for a regular expression.

Corresponding to each of the generating productions SY_a-SY_e of regular expressions, as given in Section 3, there is a translating rule to obtain recursively the ramified structure (that is, the tree) in our two-dimensional language. The rules may be applied "from the *end-points* up" or "from the *root* down."

A tree is a two-dimensional structure of the type known in combinatorial topology as an *acyclic graph*. We will scan it from top to bottom, placing the *node* called *root* at the top. It is composed of *nodes* and connecting lines called *branches*. Into each node except the root, one and only one connecting line will *descend*. The nodes from which no connecting lines descend will be called *end-points*. From each node which is not an endpoint, one or more connecting lines may descend depending upon the *stratification number* or *order* of the node. The nodes will be considered to be storage cells each capable of containing one character from a specified alphabet; each such character is assumed to have a corresponding natural number (including zero, for end-points) called its stratification number. The storage cell at a node of order n may contain only characters of stratification number n. It will be convenient, while a tree is being *constructed,* to permit characters at an end-point which do not belong to the stratified alphabet but to an auxiliary alphabet of *variables* whose values can be trees; this will permit us to generate a tree by hanging trees at end-points of already generated trees.

The trees corresponding to regular expressions are then specified as follows: The alphabet is composed of

1. Connecting lines (lengths unspecified).
2. The characters of the alphabet of the language specified by the regular expressions—for example, for the regular expression of which the triple sequence alarm is the recognizer, the alphabet is $\{0, 1\}$. Each of these characters will have stratification number zero.
3. The character "*", of stratification number one. The translation process will automatically distinguish its use in the tree language from its use in regular expressions, that is, it will automatically select its "interpretation". Similarly for the character "$\vee$", except that its stratification number is two.
4. The new character C of stratification number two, to which there corresponds the operation of "concatenation" in SY_d, but no character in the regular expression alphabet.
5. The alphabet of auxiliary variables, α, β, γ, . . . having no characters in common with the alphabet specified in 2.

The translation rules for transforming regular expressions into trees are then the following

T_{ab} The characters of the alphabet of the language specified by the regular expression (for example, 0 and 1) will be end-points.

T_c $(\alpha)^*$ will be replaced by a of Fig. 2.

T_d $\alpha\beta$ will be replaced by b of Fig. 2.

T_e $(\alpha \vee \beta)$ will be replaced by c of Fig. 2.

Although nothing is said about the order in which we recognize the applicability of or apply these translation rules, just as nothing was said about the order of application of SY_{a-e} in the generation of a regular expression, sequencing programs for them can nevertheless be designed to drive all variables out of the trees in process of generation, with an end result having only characters mentioned in 2 as end-points.

For example, our regular expression

$$\alpha = (((0 \vee 10) \vee 110))^* \, 111 \, ((0 \vee 1))^*$$

translates into the tree shown in Fig. 3.

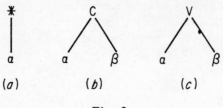

Fig. 2.

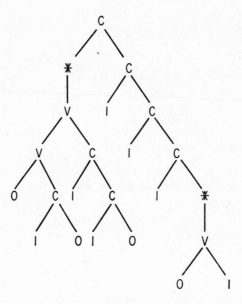

Fig. 3.

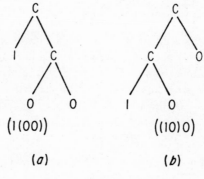

Fig. 4.

Because of the fact that we deliberately ignored the "associativity" of the $\lor$-operator (at the expense of extra parentheses, this was done to make the productions SY_{a-e} simple), there is never any doubt about the ordering of the branches following an $\lor$-*node*. Since, however, concatenation is essentially associative, choice of the possible concatenation schemes is arbitrary. For example, the tree a of Fig. 4 is *equivalent* to the tree b of Fig. 4. A regular expression has a translation into a number of trees, but they are all *equivalent*.

6. Prefix Language

Whereas our first example specified a processor, the next three each specified a language of which that processor is a recognizer. It was clear, however, that in each case, if we had used other and larger alphabets, the specifications themselves would have undergone only unessential changes. In short, we have specified families of languages, that is, language functions in which the alphabet is a free variable. Let us now present a linear sequential language (function) for the designation of trees which is more directly concerned with tree processing than, say, the original regular expressions. The type is called a *prefix language* (see Gorn 7, 8, 11).

Let us specify it by means of the translation process from the two-dimensional languages of example 4. The alphabet in each case is that of the nodes in the tree languages.

Given a tree, it may be specified in prefix language by arranging the node characters in a string as follows: Begin by placing the root character at the head of the string; after each character there are three mutually exclusive possibilities for the next character.

1. The character is not at an end-node: in this case the next character will be that immediate successor in the tree which is on the left-most branch emanating from the node.
2. The character is an end node, but is not the right-most end; in this case retrace to the first predecessor not all of whose immediate successors have been placed in the string yet and find the left-most branch which has not yet been traced; the next character to be placed on the right end of the generated string is the immediate successor on this branch.
3. The character is the right-most end node: in this case the translation is complete.

For example, the triple-sequence specifying tree of our last example has as designation in prefix language the string

$$C * \lor \lor 0 C 1 0 C 1 C 1 0 C 1 C 1 C 1 * \lor 0 1$$

In short, the order from left to right in which the node characters appear in the prefix language is the order in which a rat seeking the last end would first meet the nodes of the tree as a maze, if the rat could remember that it had already been at a node and preferred to keep to its right and to continue down.

The manner of specification of the translation process is an example of a *priority control* with an overriding priority to case 1 (see Gorn 8).

For *logical* alphabets this language will be recognized as the *Polish parenthesis-free notation,* which has also been frequently applied to "algebraic" alphabets. All the *operators* are prefixed and none is used as an infix as in the traditional notation for binary operators (for example, $x + y$).

Prefix languages systematically replace *control characters* (parentheses) by a standard scanning process, that is, certain characters may be replaced by interpreters if the *command characters* are given an appropriate scanning priority.

Such syntactic concepts as *scope of a character, depth of a character, tree address of a character,* and so on, are readily defined for prefix languages, and give rise to such standard processors as *scope analyzers, depth analyzers, tree address generators and selectors,* and so on, in addition to the usual generators and recognizers of words. There is also a simple standard production system for the specification of all prefix languages (see Gorn 8).

Oettinger 22 has also designed standard translation processors between prefix languages and corresponding languages with infix notation.

7. State Diagrams

Let us now return from examples of language specification to examples of languages for processor specification. Consider next a two-dimensional language for processor specification (mainly behavioral) called *state diagrams* (see Mealy, 17 and Moore 19). We begin by developing the state diagram of the triple sequence alarm.

We imagine that the triple sequence alarm begins in an *initial state* S_1, when it is presented with a string of zeros and ones at its input. If the input string is read from left to right, the processor will always return to state S_1 if a zero is scanned before three successive ones have appeared, that is, S_1 might be called the *disappointed state.* If the processor is in state S_1 and a one appears, there is a *transition* to *the first waiting state* S_2. If the processor is in state S_2 and a one appears, there is a transition to the *second waiting state* S_3. If the processor is in state S_3 and a one appears, there is a transition to the final state S_4. If the processor is in state S_4, all transitions are back to state S_4 whether a zero or a one appears. The state diagram is a directed graph whose nodes are marked with state names, and whose branches between nodes refer to transitions and are marked with arrows and with the output signal resulting from an input signal. Thus a state diagram for the triple sequence alarm is shown in Fig. 5.

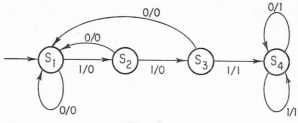

Fig. 5.

The two-dimensional language of state diagrams has the following alphabet:

1. The input signal alphabet.
2. The character "/".
3. The output signal alphabet.
4. The alphabet of *state names*.
5. The circles of variable size.
6. *Connecting arrows* of variable size.

Intermediate alphabets include

1. *State nodes* composed of circles containing state names; one marked with an initial arrow is called the *initial state*.
2. *Input-output designators* composed of strings of three characters, reading from left to right, an input alphabet character, a "/", and an output alphabet character.
3. *Transition designators* composed of a directed arrow and an input-output designator in its neighborhood and "closer" to it than to any other directed arrow.

A state diagram is composed of distinctly named nodes (no two with the same name) connected by transition designators and such that there is an exiting transition from each state for each input character. Thus the number of transitions is equal to the number of input characters times the number of states.

The procedure for translation into state diagram language of a natural language specification of a processor is at least as ill-defined as the latter.

8. Symbol-State Diagrams

The next two-dimensional language for processor specification is simpler than the state diagram in that it does not require the complicated transition designators but is more complicated in that it calls for two directed graphs per processor. If we introduce a third alphabet for transition names, then the second directed graph needed will have its nodes labeled by input-output characters instead of by state names. The state diagram for the triple sequence alarm then translates into the "symbol-state diagram" shown in Fig. 6.

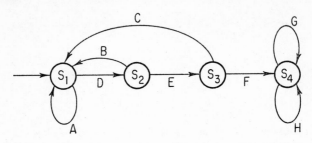

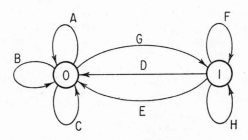

Fig. 6.

9. Incidence Matrix

Another two-dimensional language for specification of a processor is an example of a *tabular format language* such as the type used to exhibit matrices in mathematics, and double entry tables in general. It is most simply specified by a translation procedure from the symbol-state diagram language. Let us call it the language of *symbol-transition-state matrices*.

The symbol-transition matrix has its rows labeled by symbols and its columns labeled by transition names. The transition-state matrix has its rows labeled by transition names and its columns labeled by state names. The alphabet of *matrix elements* is composed of four characters: 0, $+1$, -1, and ± 1. An entry of 0 is placed at the intersection of a row and column in either matrix if the designated transition neither enters nor exits from the designated state in one case, and neither enters nor exits from the designated symbol in the other. An entry of ± 1 is placed at the appropriate cell if the transition arrow both enters and exits from the state-node or symbol-node respectively. An entry of $+1$ or -1 is placed in the appropriate cell of the appropriate matrix if the transition enters or exits, respectively, from the corresponding node in the corresponding graph.

Thus the symbol-transition-state specification of the triple sequence alarm is shown in the pair of tables.

Transition *Character*	A	B	C	D	E	F	G	H
0	± 1	± 1	± 1	$+1$	$+1$	0	-1	0
1	0	0	0	-1	-1	± 1	$+1$	± 1

State *Transition*	S_1	S_2	S_3	S_4
A	± 1	0	0	0
B	$+1$	-1	0	0
C	$+1$	0	-1	0
D	-1	$+1$	0	0
E	0	-1	$+1$	0
F	0	0	-1	$+1$
G	0	0	0	± 1
H	0	0	0	± 1

The language for either matrix could have been simplified to use only a binary entry alphabet {0, 1}. For the symbol-transition matrix, this would require distinguishing input and output characters, and having a separate row for each. For the transition-state matrix, it would call for a distinction between *states-on-entry* and *states-on-exit* and would require a separate column for each.

There are a number of well-known algorithms for processing these *incidence-matrices* and also for the derivation of *path-matrices* and *connection matrices*. These algorithms yield results useful in switching theory (Hohn [13, 14]), combinatorial topology (Veblen [23]), and graph theory (Berge [1]).

10. Logical Net

The next language type we consider is again two-dimensional, can specify simultaneous action, and is most useful for structural specifications of processors. Languages of this type are therefore much used in logical design (Burks-Copi 3, Burks-Wright 2, Wilkes 24, and so on).

As a simplified example, let us specify one called *logical net language*.

The logical net language is a two-dimensional language with the following alphabet

1. An alphabet of *gate-type designators*—we will use the characters $\vee$, $\wedge$, and $\sim$, calling them OR, AND, and NOT, respectively; each character of this alphabet has a "stratification number", 1 for $\sim$, and 2 for $\wedge$ and $\vee$.
2. An alphabet of *delay designators*—in our example we will use $\{j, k\}$.
3. An alphabet of *wire designators*—in our example we will use $\{i, j, k, p, q, r, s, u, v, w.$
4. A rectangular box of fixed size, called a *delay*, and designating a unit time interval between *entrance* and *exit*.
5. A circle of fixed size, called a *gate*.
6. Connecting lines of varying size with an arrow head at one end, called *wires*.
7. A *dot* called an AND-*node*, and designating simultaneous continuations of a wire in a number of directions.
8. A "$\cup$" symbol in a variety of orientations to designate the nonconnection of crossing wires.

Among the intermediate alphabets we might mention

1. *Gate-designators* composed of gates containing a gate-type character—thus $\ominus$ is a NOT-*gate*, $\varnothing$ is an OR-*gate*, $\oslash$ is an AND-*gate*.
2. *Delay symbols* composed of a delay rectangle containing a delay designator.
3. *Delay elements* composed of a delay symbol with one input wire and one output wire.
4. *Gate elements* are gates with one *output wire* and a number of *input wires* equal to the stratification number of the gate type designator in the gate designator.

A logical net, then, is a two-dimensional connected array of these elements in which wires intersect only at AND-nodes and not at $\cup$-symbols. At each time unit it is assumed that each wire is "transmitting" one of two signals designated by 0 and 1, respectively. For example, Fig. 7 illustrates a logical net for the triple sequence alarm.

Here i marks the unique *input wire* and u the unique *output wire*. A logical net containing no delay elements is called a *combinational net*. For example, the net contained in the dotted box marked C is a combinational net with three input wires (i, j, k), and three output wires (u, v, w). A logical net which is not a combinational net is called a *sequential net*.

There is a heuristic translation procedure permitting one to translate from the behavioral specification of a processor which is provided by a state diagram into a structural specification of that processor in the logical net language. Let us illustrate this translation procedure for the triple sequence alarm.

First of all, there is the theorem to the effect that a logical net containing n unit delays corresponds to a processor having 2^n states. Second, there is a *normal-form* theorem to the effect that every net with I inputs, U outputs and D delay units is equivalent to a net constructed from a combinational

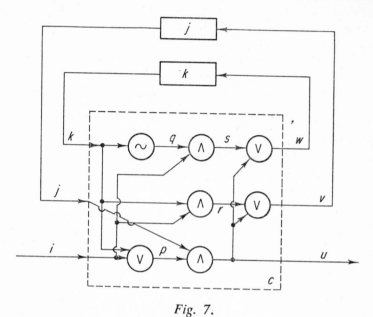

Fig. 7.

net C with $I + D$ inputs and $U + D$ outputs where D inputs and D outputs are paired to feed back from an output of C through a delay and back into the corresponding input of C. The net in the diagram of Fig. 7 is an example.

Thus the triple sequence alarm, having four states, requires a minimum of two delays, j and k, with outputs similarly marked. Let their inputs be v and w respectively, and let state S_1 correspond to outputs $j = 0$, $k = 0$; S_2 to $j = 0$, $k = 1$; S_3 to $j = 1$, $k = 0$; and S_4 to $j = 1$, $k = 1$. The triple sequence alarm calls for an output 1 only for the three transitions F, G, and H, so that $u = 1$ if and only if either $j = k = 1$ (for G and H from state S_4) or $i = 1$ and $j = 1$, $k = 0$ (for F from state S_3; in other words, the required combinational net C must have $u = jk + ij\bar{k} = j(i + k)$ in the notation of boolean algebra. This condition on u was therefore obtained by examining the entrances into state S_4. Now consider the entrances into all states for which $j = 1$, that is the states S_3 and S_4 via the transitions E, F, G, and H; the transition E occurs when the input is 1 $(i = 1)$ and the preceding state was S_3 $(j = 0, k = 1)$; hence $v = 1$ if and only if either $i = 1$, $j = 0$, and $k = 1$, or $j(i + k) = 1$ as before; this yields the condition $v = i\bar{j}k + j(i + k)$ which "simplifies" to $v = ik + j(i + k)$. Finally, the entrances into all states for which $k = 1$ is provided by the transitions D, F, G, H, yielding $w = i\bar{j}k + j(i + k)$ because D is marked for an input 1 at state S_1 where $j = k = 0$; manipulation in boolean algebra permits us to *simplify* this condition into $w = i\bar{k} + j(i + k)$.

Rewriting these three conditions with our net operators then yields the following behavioral specification of the required combinational net C

$$u = [j \wedge (i \vee k)],$$
$$v = [j \wedge (i \vee k)] \vee (i \wedge k),$$
$$w = [j \wedge (i \vee k)] \vee (i \wedge \sim k).$$

These behavioral specifications can be met economically by introducing intermediate gates and lines as follows

$$p = i \vee k$$
$$q = \sim k$$
$$r = i \wedge k$$
$$s = i \wedge q$$

to yield

$$u = j \wedge p$$
$$v = u \vee r$$
$$w = u \vee s$$

Thus a NOT-gate is needed from k, and an AND-node is needed from k to lead to an input to the AND-gate for r and to the OR-gate for p. Similarly, an AND-node is needed to lead to another input of the AND-gate for r and to an input of the AND-gate for s, whose other input is q. Finally, AND-nodes are needed from u to the OR-gates yielding v and w from the other inputs r and s respectively.

These detailed requirements yield the complete logical net.

11. Propositional Logic with a Time Variable

We can now specify a descriptive linear, simultaneous action language within which we can provide structural specifications of sequential processors. This is the language of *propositional logic with time as a variable*.

The language of propositional logic with time as a variable has the following alphabet

1. An alphabet of ordinal numbers to designate time units.
2. The characters $-$ and $+$ to designate time unit differences in the past or in the future.
3. The character t to designate a variable instant of time.
4. The control characters "(" and ")" for the construction of *signal designators* and the bracketing of *logical expressions*.
5. A *logical operator* alphabet, for example, $\sim$, $\wedge$, and $\vee$ to designate NOT, AND, and OR, respectively.
6. The character "$=$" to designate the declarative verb *is identical as a signal with*.
7. The control character ";" to serve as a statement separator.
8. An alphabet of *wire names* (for example, p, q, . . .), but not to include t.

Intermediate languages (syntactic types) will include

1. ⟨Signal designator⟩ $::= $ ⟨wire name⟩ (⟨time designator⟩).
2. ⟨Time designator⟩ $::= t \,|\, t -$ ⟨ordinal⟩ $\,|\, t +$ ⟨ordinal⟩.
3. ⟨Logical expression⟩ to be similar to those of logic, but using the alphabet of signal designators as variables.
4. ⟨Statement⟩ $::= $ ⟨signal desinator⟩ $= $ ⟨logical expression⟩.

A mechanical procedure can be specified to translate from the logical net language into the language of propositional logic with time as a variable. When applied to the triple sequence alarm it yields the following specification

$$u(t) = p(t) \wedge j(t); \quad p(t) = i(t) \vee k(t); \quad v(t) = u(t) \vee r(t);$$
$$r(t) = i(t) \wedge k(t); \quad w(t) = s(t) \vee u(t); \quad s(t) = q(t) \wedge i(t);$$
$$q(t) = \sim k(t); \quad j(t) = v(t-1); \quad k(t) = w(t-1)$$

This specification can be manipulated in various ways to eliminate various wires which are not inputs or outputs of C. It can also be manipulated (algebraically) to yield the output as a function of the input and supply a check against an initial behavioral specification of a processor.

12. Logical Equations

The language of propositional logic with time as a variable may be mechanically translated into a mixed (descriptive and command), linear, simultaneous action language for structural specification of processors. This language has been called *logical equations* (see Gorn-Ingerman-Crozier 12).

The alphabet of logical equations adds to that of propositional logic with time as a variable the following characters

1. 0 and 1 to designate the *base alphabet* of the processor, that is, its two signal levels.
2. "$\rightarrow$" to designate the imperative verb (command) *transmit to*.

3. "$\equiv>$" to designate the causal relationship between having such and such a state and having such and such a transmission occur—this is a *control verb*.

Important sublanguages (*clauses*) are, then

1. $\langle$signal$\rangle$ ::= 0 | 1
2. $\langle$action clause$\rangle$ ::= $\langle$signal$\rangle$ → $\langle$signal designator$\rangle$
3. $\langle$state clause$\rangle$ ::= $\langle$logical expression$\rangle$ = $\langle$signal designator$\rangle$
4. $\langle$control sentence$\rangle$ ::= $\langle$state clause$\rangle$ $\equiv>$ $\langle$action clause$\rangle$

Although other systems of logical equations might be more *economical* in specifying a processor, one can always be obtained by immediate translation from a specification in the language of propositional logic with time as a variable by transforming each statement: $\langle$signal designator$\rangle$ = $\langle$logical expression$\rangle$ into the control sentence: $\langle$logical expression$\rangle$ = 1 $\equiv>$ 1 → $\langle$signal designator$\rangle$. Thus the specification of the triple sequence alarm would begin as follows

$$p(t) \wedge j(t) = 1 \equiv> 1 \to u(t)$$
$$i(t) \vee k(t) = 1 \equiv> 1 \to p(t) \text{ etc.}$$

This language is clearly equivalent to a two-column tabular format language in which states in logical equation form are entered in the first column and the corresponding actions are entered in the second column.

13. Turing Machines

The next language class has already been of great theoretical utility in the foundations of mathematics and logic. It is that group of languages in which *Turing machines* are specified (see Davis, 6 Moore, 20 and Minsky 18). In the idealized forms needed for the theory it is assumed that there is available a machine which can be in a number of states S_1, S_2, ... and which scans one or more *tapes*, each a sequential arrangement of *cells* capable of containing one character each of an alphabet called *symbols*. Actions result from a state and an input symbol, and in the idealized forms these actions are composed of transitions to other states, motions of the tape or tapes one cell to the right or left, erasures in cells, and placing new symbols in cells. A specification language for Turing machines must therefore begin with the following alphabets

1. State names
2. Symbols
3. Special action names, for example, R and L for move tape right or left.

The language itself can then be specified in a manner similar to that in example 12 above, or in the two-column tabular format mentioned there.

The triple sequence alarm may be specified in this manner if we assume

1. An *input tape* which always moves one cell to the right at each action, and whose current cell is the storage position i.
2. An *output tape* which always moves one cell to the right at each action, and whose current cell is the storage position u.
3. Either the state name alphabet of the state diagram above, S_1, S_2, S_3, S_4, or the state name alphabet $(jk) = (00)$, (01), (10), (11), of the corresponding outputs of the pair of delay elements in the logical net above; let us call the two delays d_1 and d_2, and consider them one-bit storage cells whose contents last one time unit each.

The specification of the triple sequence alarm can therefore simplify into either of the tables shown.

State d_1d_2:	*Symbol* i	*New State* d_1d_2:	*Output Symbol* u
0 0	0	0 0	0
0 0	1	0 1	0
0 1	0	0 0	0
0 1	1	1 0	0
1 0	0	0 0	0
1 0	1	1 1	1
1 1	0	1 1	1
1 1	1	1 1	1

	S_1	S_2	S_3	S_4
0	$S_1 0$	$S_1 0$	$S_1 0$	$S_4 1$
1	$S_2 0$ ·	$S_3 0$	$S_4 1$	$S_4 1$

14. Flow Chart

The last language class we would like to list for processor specification (structural) is the two-dimensional sequential command language class called *flow charts* which is much used by programmers. Such languages may be simultaneously acting, as in *micro-flowcharts*, or purely sequential. One such language is specified in Gorn [10] together with a translation procedure to the linear sequential command languages known as *machine codes.* A translation procedure from *logical equations* into micro-flowcharts is described in Gorn-Ingerman-Crozier [12].

The flow-chart languages are good to exhibit at a glance the main *control flow* of a program; the *data flow*, however, though specified completely, is certainly not obvious. Control transformations of data into commands sometimes are obvious (as in programmed switches) and sometimes are not (as in variable instructions which are *computed*).

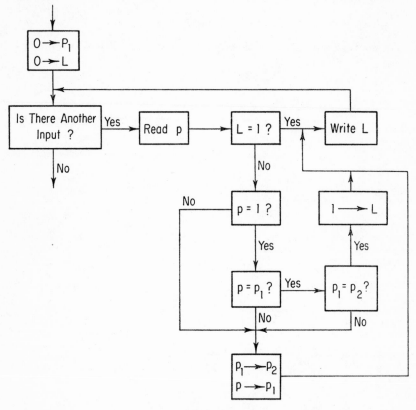

Fig. 8.

Processors may be *simulated* (that is, specified by a program which only partially translates their full specification) at many levels of detail, from the bit logic at micro-level, through the behavior at register level (as in an *interpreter* or an *automonitor*), into a simulation of the behavioral specifications only (that is, of input-output behavior only). The flow chart in Fig. 8 shows an input-output simulator of the triple sequence alarm: the *current input bit* is stored in p, the preceding one in p_1, and the one before that in p_2. The current output signal is stored in L.

A specification in flow-chart language of a translation processor from the linear language of algebraic expressions to a linear language of *machine code* may be found in Wegstein 26.

Acknowledgment

The author wishes to thank Frank A. Williams, Jr. for his help with the Introduction.

References

1. C. Berge, *Théorie des Graphes et ses Applications*, Dunod, Paris (1959).

2. A. W. Burks, and J. B. Wright, "Theory of Logical Nets," *Proc. IRE;* Vol. 41 (1953), pp. 1357–1365.

3. A. W. Burks, and I. M. Copi, "The Logical Design of an Idealized General-Purpose Computer," *J. Franklin Inst.* Vol. 261 (1956), pp. 299–314, 421–436.

4. N. Chomsky, "On Certain Formal Properties of Grammars," *Informat. Contr.* Vol. 2 (June 1959), pp. 137–167.

5. N. Chomsky, "Three Models for the Description of Language," *IRE Trans. Informat. Theory.* Vol. IT-2, 3 (Sept. 1956), pp. 113-124.

6. M. Davis, *Computability and Unsolvability*, McGraw-Hill, New York (1958).

7. S. Gorn, "Common Programming Language Task," Pt. I, Sec. 5. Final Report AD59URI, The Moore School of Electrical Engineering, University of Pennsylvania (July 31, 1959). Available from Defense Documentation Center as AD 236-997.

8. S. Gorn, "Common Programming Language Task," Pt. I. Final Report, AD60URI, The Moore School of Electrical Engineering, University of Pennsylvania (June 30, 1960). Available from Defense Documentation Center as AD 248-110.

9. S. Gorn, "Some Basic Terminology Connected with Mechanical Languages and Their Processors," *Comm. ACM.* Vol. 4 (August 1961).

10. S. Gorn, "Standardized Programming Methods and Universal Coding," *J. ACM.* Vol. 4 (July 1957), pp. 254–273.

11. S. Gorn, "The Treatment of Ambiguity and Paradox in Mechanical Languages," *Proc. Symposia in Pure Mathematics,* American Mathematical Society (1962).

12. S. Gorn, P. Z. Ingerman, and J. B. Crozier, "On the Construction of Micro-Flowcharts," *Comm. ACM.* Vol. 2 (October 1959), pp. 27–31.

13. F. E. Hohn, "Boolean Matrices and the Design of Combinational Relay Switching Circuit," *Bell System Tech. J.* Vol. 34 (January 1955), pp. 177–202.

14. F. E. Hohn, S. Seshu, and D. D. Aufenkamp, "The Theory of Nets," *IRE Trans. Electr. Comput.* Vol. EC-6 (1957), pp. 154–161.

15. S. C. Kleene, "Representation of Events in Nerve Nets and Finite Automata," *Automata Studies,* ed. C. E. Shannon and J. McCarthy, Princeton University Press, Princeton, New Jersey (1956), pp. 3–41.

16. R. McNaughton, and H. Yamada, "Regular Expressions and State Graphs for Automata," WADC TN 59-192, U.S. Air Force Contract AF 33 (616)-5886; The Moore School of Electrical Engineering, University of Pennsylvania, Report No. 60-06 (July 1, 1959).

17. G. H. Mealy, "Method of Synthesizing Sequential Circuits," *Bell System Tech. J.* Vol. 34 (September 1955), pp. 1045–1079.

18. M. Minsky, "A 6-Symbol 7-State Universal Turing Machine," Report No. 54G-0027 Contract AF 19(604)5200 (August 17, 1960), Lincoln Lab., MIT.

19. E. F. Moore, "Gedanken-Experiments on Sequential Machines," *Automata Studies,* ed. C. E. Shannon and J. McCarthy, Princeton University Press, Princeton, New Jersey (1956), pp. 129–153.

20. E. F. Moore, "A Simplified Universal Turing Machine," presented to the Association for Computing Machinery (1952).

21. P. Naur, (ed.), "Report on the Algorithmic Language ALGOL 60," *Comm. ACM*, Vol. 3 (May 1960), pp. 299–314.

22. A. G. Oettinger, "Automatic Syntactic Analysis and the Pushdown Store," *Proc. Symposia in Applied Mathematics*, American Mathematical Society (1961).

23. O. Veblen, *Analysis Situs*, American Mathematical Society, New York (1931).

24. M. V. Wilkes, *Automatic Digital Computers*, Methuen, London (1957).

25. J. W. Backus, "The Syntax and Semantics of the Proposed International Algebraic Language of the Zurich ACM-GAMM Conference," presented at the First International Conference on Information Processing (ICIP) June 13–23, 1959 in Paris, France. International Business Machines Corp., New York.

26. J. Wegstein, "A General Purpose Pseudocode," Annual ACM Conf., Ann Arbor, Mich. (June 1954).

A more extensive bibliography and further discussion of some of these languages may be found in:

27. R. McNaughton, "The Theory of Automata—a Survey," *Advances in Computers,* Vol. 2, Franz L. Alt (ed.), Academic Press, New York (1961).

3   Natural Language in Computer Form

Martin Kay and Theodore Ziehe

1. Introduction

The problem of obtaining texts in a form the machine can read is in many ways more vexing than that of programming. Hitherto, it has always been necessary to type out any text to be processed by a computer on a special machine which produces a coded copy of it on punched cards or on paper tape. This is particularly burdensome since the gains in speed and accuracy which come with the use of computers can all too easily be offset if large bodies of text have to be typed out by the researcher or an assistant, proofread, corrected, and modified.

As text coded on tapes and cards becomes more plentiful, thanks to use of computers in the publication industry, libraries of such materials will doubtless be established, as they have been for microfilm, phonograph records, and the like. Each year, the chance will be greater that the text required by a particular scholar will already have been put into machine form.

This brings us face to face with our central concern—the question of standards for natural-language text in machine-readable form. To serve linguistic and literary studies as it ought to, machine-readable text must become as public as books, phonograph records, and films. However, to make a commodity public, it is not always sufficient to put it on the open market. A phonograph record which had to be played at 54 rpm would not be really public; neither would an otherwise perfectly normal English newspaper if the letters on each line were arranged from right to left instead of from left to right. It is therefore important that there be general agreement upon the form in which information is to be published.

Standard forms are already fairly well established for the grosser aspects of machine-readable material. The size and shape of punched cards are

Note: This research was sponsored by the United States Air Force under Project RAND—Contract No. AF 49(638)-700 monitored by the Directorate of Development Plans, Deputy Chief of Staff, Research and Development, Hq. USAF. This portion of Memorandum RM-4390-PR (February 1965) is reprinted with permission of the authors and The RAND Corporation, Santa Monica, California.

standard, and most manufacturers of computers, at least in the United States, use the same size of magnetic tape and the same kind of associated recording equipment. Most punched paper tape conforms to one of four standards, of which one is slowly gaining the ascendancy. However, machines are available which can be used to read paper tape of all four kinds.

On the other hand, there are not yet any standards for transcribing texts in ordinary language onto any of these media. How shall chapters, sections, and paragraphs be set off from one another? How are titles, subtitles, captions, and footnotes to be represented? What is to be done with scientific and mathematical formulae? How shall the distinctions among italics, boldface, and underlining be preserved? What of accented letters and unusual alphabets? Of course, these are questions which arise whenever we transcribe anything but the simplest kind of text on an ordinary typewriter, for an ordinary typewriter can make only a limited set of marks. But where the computer is concerned, we are denied the typist's ultimate resort of inserting exotic characters by hand. Furthermore, the conventions used for the computer must be carefully chosen and meticulously followed because the computer does not have the human facility for making inferences from context or for overlooking minor inconsistencies of convention. Good conventions are difficult to establish, and this, in itself, is good reason for having a standard, well-designed set which all may use.

But how can standard conventions for recording text be established when the physical form of the media used varies from place to place and from time to time? Some people use cards and some paper tape; some feed cards or tape directly into the computer whenever they wish to process it, whereas most first transfer material to magnetic tape or disk, which can be processed more rapidly by a large computer and is more easily stored. A limited amount of information can be punched on a single card, whereas there is much greater freedom with tape.

This disparity is indeed troublesome, but less so than at first appears. If large libraries of machine-readable text are to be built up, the principal storage medium used must clearly be cheap, flexible, widely used, durable, compact, and of essentially unlimited capacity. Among the media available at present, magnetic tape best meets these criteria. Furthermore, as we shall see, the fact that text must be recorded on cards or paper tape before transfer to magnetic tape is an advantage rather than a drawback of this medium.

Consider the case of a man who is working on the New Testament and wishes to use a computer to perform certain operations on the Greek text. A general set of text-encoding conventions must clearly provide for texts which use the Greek alphabet, even though machines which have these symbols on their keyboards are rare. Normally, a transliteration scheme must be used at the keyboard and a computer program used to convert this into the standard format. The person who does the typing or keypunching can choose the transliteration which he finds easiest to use, and he need not concern himself with inserting marks to warn the machine that certain characters are to be interpreted in special ways. In any case, a program must be used to transfer the text from the medium on which it is originally punched onto magnetic tape, and this program can be made to do all the necessary conversions. The program can be provided with a table telling it that the text is in Greek and giving the transliteration scheme; it must also be told how chapter and verse divisions are being marked and various other clerical details of this kind. The important point is that the standard format need not be an additional burden to the typist or keypuncher. On the other hand, the designer of the standard format need not be constrained by a concern for the typist. A truly general set of coding conventions is unlikely to be easy to read and write, and it is therefore well that it should never need to be handled in its full complexity by anything but a computer program.

In many ways, printing text is similar to typing it. When a computer prints a text, or the results of some operations on a text, it must not be required to follow a single, invariable set of rules. Here again, a program intervenes to prepare results in the form most suited to the user's needs, using his own conventions, transliterations, and page layout. Magnetic tape is just sufficiently remote from the everyday concerns of the user to provide him with the generality and flexibility he needs without troubling him with all the details. Once he has decided which of the facilities provided in the system he needs and has set up the necessary input and printing programs, he is free to work in his own way.

If a library of machine-readable text were set up for the benefit of a number of users or if one person had a particularly large amount of information to process, then the question of how to keep track of it all would soon arise. It would be necessary to divide the lines of text into units analogous to chapters, books, and collections of related books. Each of these divisions would have to be appropriately labeled so that it could be referred to easily and found when required, so material could be changed, corrected, or modified and so other material could be put in the file before or after it. With such a system would come the need to store a new kind of information which would not be true text but rather information about the text—names of sections, acquisition dates, names of people who have modified or corrected a certain piece of text, indexing information, and so forth. All these things are provided for in the scheme described in this article, in the form of a simple but powerful set of overall conventions.

2. Codes

A printed page contains letters of whatever sizes, colors, and shapes the typographer's art puts at the service of author, designer, and editor. A magnetic tape—as furnished, for example, by IBM—contains nothing but a very long sequence of binary digits (bits), ones and zeros, blocked in units of 6. The purpose of the somewhat complex codes described in the present section is to simplify the representation of textual matter in binary form. One should not attempt to keep in mind at every moment the configuration of ones and zeros that represent, say, a Greek alpha or a mathematician's integral sign. Nor would it be convenient to specify a 10-, 11-, or 12-bit pattern for each of the thousand or more characters that must somehow be represented.

2.1. Hollerith Characters

If we use 6 bits as the basic unit, there will be exactly 64 distinguishable patterns, and one of 64 *characters* can be recorded in each unit. Since it is inconvenient to write out 6-bit patterns in discussing machine operation, the customary scheme is to use *octal* digits to stand for 3-bit patterns. Table 1 shows the correspondence. Thus, the name of "000000" is "00," the name of "000001" is "01," and so on. The name of "111111" is "77."

Table 1. Binary Patterns and Octal Digits

Binary	Octal	Binary	Octal
000	0	100	4
001	1	101	5
010	2	110	6
011	3	111	7

A reader who is not familiar with binary and octal numbers can best regard the 64 names assigned in this way as perfectly arbitrary.

The 64 characters can be copied from magnetic tape into the storage device of an electronic computer and copied from storage onto tape. Only 48 of them can normally be printed on paper for a human reader; for many years, printers controlled by punched cards were designed to print 48 different marks, and the tradition has continued. The 48 standard marks include the letters of the Roman alphabet, the 10 decimal digits, a few marks of punctuation, arithmetic signs, and a blank. The other 16 characters that can be recorded on magnetic tape but are not normally printed are designated here by their numbers. Table 2 associates the binary pat-

Table 2. Binary Patterns, Octal Equivalents, and Hollerith Marks

B	O	H	B	O	H	B	O	H	B	O	H	B	O	H
000 000	00	0	001 101	15		011 010	32		100 111	47	P	110 100	64	U
000 001	01	1	001 110	16		011 011	33	.	101 000	50	Q	110 101	65	V
000 010	02	2	001 111	17		011 100	34	)	101 001	51	R	110 110	66	W
000 011	03	3	010 000	20	+	011 101	35		101 010	52		110 111	67	X
000 100	04	4	010 001	21	A	011 110	36		101 011	53	$	111 000	70	Y
000 101	05	5	010 010	22	B	011 111	37		101 100	54	*	111 001	71	Z
000 110	06	6	010 011	23	C	100 000	40	–	101 101	55		111 010	72	
000 111	07	7	010 100	24	D	100 001	41	J	101 110	56		111 011	73	
001 000	10	8	010 101	25	E	100 010	42	K	101 111	57		111 100	74	,
001 001	11	9	010 110	26	F	100 011	43	L	110 000	60ª		111 101	75	(
001 010	12		010 111	27	G	100 100	44	M	110 001	61	/	111 110	76	
001 011	13	=	011 000	30	H	100 101	45	N	110 010	62	S	111 111	77	
001 100	14	'	011 001	31	I	100 110	46	O	110 011	63	T			

ª Octal 60 corresponds to the Hollerith blank.

terns, the octal equivalents, and the 48 Hollerith characters that we have been discussing.

Tradition is strong, but modern necessities are stronger. The 48 Hollerith characters are no longer the only ones that can be printed. Other sets of 48, sets of 120, and even sets of 240 are now obtainable. In fact, direct output to machines with all the flexibility of Linotype or Monotype machines is possible. This very powerful printing capability provides added incentive to develop a flexible encoding scheme.

Since the design of most computing machines compels us to work with 64 primitive characters, we have two feasible alternatives for the recording of ordinary texts in which a much larger character set is used. We may represent each distinct printer's mark with a sequence of two or more recordable characters or we may adopt the functional equivalent of the case shift on a typewriter. When the shift lock on the typewriter is depressed, the effect of striking a key is altered. Each key is associated with two marks; one mark is obtained when the machine is in its lowercase shift, the other when it is in uppercase. The number of shifts can be increased beyond two, and their use can be extended, for example, to the differentiation of Greek and Roman letters.

2.2. The Roman Alphabet

The 64 recordable characters are distributed by standard machines into a set of 48 that can be printed and a set of 16 that cannot. We take 15 of the nonprintable characters as *alphabet flags*. The flag for the Roman alphabet is (octal) 35 = (binary) 011101. After an occurrence of this flag, all following characters on a tape are taken to represent letters of the Roman alphabet until another alphabet flag occurs to signal a shift into a different alphabet.

The Roman alphabet is intended for use in transcribing English text, as well as French, German, Portuguese, Rumanian, and others. The 26 letters of the English alphabet are therefore supplemented by ten diacritics. Most punctuation is excluded from the Roman alphabet, to be kept in another (a "punctuation" alphabet), but one mark, the apostrophe, has been retained.

Five characters are used to identify special fonts of type. These identifiers can also be thought of as shift indicators. They can be used singly or in combination to modify the characters in the current alphabet. The absence of any font identifier is understood to mean lowercase, standard font. An identifier is reserved for uppercase, another for italics or script, a third for bold face, one for larger type than ordinary, and one for smaller type. Strung together, they can identify words or phrases in several font combinations, for example, bold-face italics, all caps small size, large-size italics. Three characters are used to identify sequences of marks that are printed as superscripts or subscripts with respect to the ordinary line or with letter spacing in the European manner. Still another character is used to identify the end of any one or combination of the shifts described here.

To complete the set of 48 recordable characters, the Roman alphabet includes a space and an unassigned character.

As examples of use of shift indicators within the Roman alphabet, consider the following encoding; the first line is from source text, the second is Hollerith representation of the characters on magnetic tape:

We seek the coöperation of all men of good will.
1W9E SEEK THE CO–OPERATION OF ALL MEN OF GOOD WILL
C'était à l'époque de NAPOLEON que le héro est né.
1C9'(ETAIT) A L'(EPOQUE DE 1NAPOLEON9 QUE LE H(ERO EST N(E

Smith$_a$ and Jones$_b$ have *disagreed* violently
1S9MITH6A9 AND 1J9ONES6B9 HAVE 2DISAGREED9 VIOLENTLY

In these examples, terminal periods have been omitted from the Hollerith representations. Punctuation belongs in another alphabet and would require flags, use of which is demonstrated in Sec. 2.5. Table 3 recapitulates the coding of the Roman alphabet.

Table 3. Code: Roman Alphabet[a]

	Letters								Diacritics			Shifts		
T	O	H	T	O	H	T	O	H	T	O	H	T	O	H
A	21	A	J	41	J	S	62	S	ó	74	(	Uppercase	01	1
B	22	B	K	42	K	T	63	T	ò	34	)	Italics or Script	02	2
C	23	C	L	43	L	U	64	U	ö	13	=	Boldface	03	3
D	24	D	M	44	M	V	65	V	ç	73	,	Larger Size	04	4
E	25	E	N	45	N	W	66	W	ô	20	+	Smaller Size	05	5
F	26	F	O	46	O	X	67	X	õ	53	$	Superscript	06	6
G	27	G	P	47	P	Y	70	Y	ǒ	54	*	Subscript	07	7
H	30	H	Q	50	Q	Z	71	Z	å	33	.	Letter Spacing	10	8
I	31	I	R	51	R	'	14	'	ō	40	–	Shift Terminator	11	9
									ø	61	/	Blank	60	

[a] Column headings: T = text, O = octal, H = Hollerith. In German text, β is encoded as 73-62, that is, S with cedilla. In the presentation of diacritics in this table, the letter is used only to provide a base; the diacritic is encoded independently of the letter it accompanies, as on a typewriter with dead keys.

2.3. The Cyrillic Alphabet

The Cyrillic alphabet, used for transcription of Russian text, includes 32 letters. Since no diacritics are needed, there is no difficulty about fitting this alphabet into a set of 48 recordable characters. In addition to the Cyrillic letters, there are represented an apostrophe, a blank, the shift indicators used in the Roman alphabet, and the terminator needed to identify the end of any shift or combination of shifts. Five characters are left unassigned. The code is given in Table 4.

Table 4. Code: Cyrillic Alphabet[a]

T	O	H	X	T	O	H	X	T	O	H	X	T	O	H	X
А	14	'	A	Й	31	I	J	Т	50	Q	T	Ы	67	X	Y
Б	21	A	B	К	34	)	K	У	51	R	U	Ь	70	Y	'
В	22	B	V	Л	41	J	L	Ф	53	$	F	Э	71	Z	,
Г	23	C	G	М	42	K	M	Х	54	*	X	Ю	73	,	(
Д	24	D	D	Н	43	L	N	Ц	62	S	C	Я	74	(	=
Е	25	E	E	О	44	M	O	Ч	63	T	H	'	13	=	)
Ж	26	F	*	П	45	N	P	Ш	64	U	W				
З	27	G	Z	Р	46	O	R	Щ	65	V	Q				
И	30	H	I	С	47	P	S	Ъ	66	W	$				

a Column headings: T = text, O = octal, H = Hollerith, X = transliteration. Shifts and blank are treated exactly as in the Roman alphabet (see Table 3). No Cyrillic diacritics are provided.

In the following example, the first line is from source text, the second is Hollerith representation of the characters on magnetic tape, and the third is Hollerith-character transliteration of the tape records. Again, alphabet flags are not shown.

Пучок протонов из электростатического генератора
1N9RTM) NOMQMLMB HG ZJE)QOMPQ'QHTEP)MCM CELEO'QMO'
1P9UHOK PROTONOV IZ ,LEKTROSTATIHESKOGO GENERATORA

2.4. Punctuation and Boundaries

An alphabet of punctuation marks is included in the present system to allow unambiguous representation on tape of the many marks that occur in text. Table 5 lists the marks for which characters have been assigned; 17 additional marks can be added to the alphabet at will.

Two linguistic boundaries are given special status for the benefit of editors who choose to mark sentences and paragraphs in their text files.

Table 5. Code: Punctuation[a]

	Text	Octal	Hollerith
(	Open Parenthesis	74	(
)	Close Parenthesis	34	)
"	Open Quotation Mark (Double)	21	A
"	Close Quotation Mark (Double)	22	B
'	Open Quotation Mark (Single)	23	C
'	Close Quotation Mark (Single)	24	D
[	Open Brackets	25	E
]	Close Brackets	26	F
<<	Open Double Angles	27	G
>>	Close Double Angles	30	H
.	Period	33	.
:	Colon	31	I
;	Semicolon	41	J
,	Comma	73	,
-	Hyphen	40	-
—	Dash	47	P
?	Question Mark	42	K
¿	Open Question Mark (Spanish)	43	L
!	Exclamation Mark	44	M
¡	Open Exclamation (Spanish)	45	N
...	Ellipsis	46	0
/	Slash	61	/
	Space	60	

[a] Shift codes are the same as in the Roman alphabet (see Table 3), except that no uppercase shift is provided.

These two boundaries are represented by two characters in a boundary alphabet (Table 6) which is otherwise free for uses yet to be defined.

Table 6. Code: Boundaries

Text	Octal	Hollerith
Beginning of Paragraph	47	P
Beginning of Sentence	62	S
Space	60	

2.5. Flags, Shifts, and Fillers

Some of the 64 characters that can be recorded on tape are used to represent printed marks; the others are either flags or shifts. The flag characters are not said to belong to any alphabet; the shift characters belong to every alphabet. This difference reflects the fact that shifts are part of the linguistic description of a text, whereas flags are only a computational device.

Flags are defined because our tape machines record and recognize 6-bit patterns. Only flag characters have independent definitions; the meaning of a flag is always the same, regardless of context. Each flag signifies that the following nonflag, or *text,* characters are to be interpreted by reference to a certain alphabet. Table 7 shows the flag codes and the alphabets that they designate.

Table 7. Code: Alphabet Flags

Alphabet	Octal
Roman	35
Cyrillic	36
Greek	37
Symbols	55
Cover Symbols	56
Punctuation	15
Boundaries	16
Filler	77

The shifts that we define are *graphemes.* It is true that their use could be avoided if we had a sufficiently large set of recordable characters, but using them has advantages beyond mere reduction of the size of the character set. For example, consultation of a dictionary is more convenient if the same word, printed in normal type in one place and in bold face elsewhere, is spelled with the same characters in both places. Isolation of a *bold face* grapheme gives us this advantage without losing the information about type style.

The shift graphemes could have been defined in several ways. Thus, the *range* of a shift could extend (1) over a single letter, (2) over all letters up to the following blank, (3) over all letters up to the next shift or the next shift in a given class, (4) over all letters up to a terminator specific to the given shift, or (5) over all letters up to a generalized terminator. In our choice of the fifth plan, three criteria of simplicity were relevant: size of alphabet, length of text, and complexity of rules. Plans 1 and 2 would save one character, the terminator, but lengthen the text; and Plan 2 would not permit encoding of, for example, "*un*happiness." Plan 3 would require introduction of a *normal* shift, perhaps several, in place of the terminator. Plan 4 would call for more terminators; it would tend to shorten text, as when a word is italicized within a bold-face line, but such occurrences are rare.

It is important to understand that shifts can be used in combination. For example, we have already noted that bold-face italic can be represented by two shift indicators preceding a string of characters, but it is also possible to use a string of identical shifts to represent an extreme degree of an attribute. Thus, X6Y6Z represents x^{y^z} and X6Y7Z represents an occurrence of x with a superscript composed of y with subscripted z. Of course, if the occurrence of z were back on the principal line, the encoded representation would be X6Y9Z. In similar fashion, LOOK encodes a word in normal-size type, 4LOOK encodes a word in large type, 44LOOK encodes a word in still larger type, and so on. Naturally, the editor of a text will not attempt to distinguish more sizes than are essential to retain the meaning.

Of the 64 characters recordable on tape, only one remains to be explained; it serves as a filler. The 6-bit patterns on magnetic tape are recorded and read in groups of 6. Naturally, it is not always possible to code a segment of text so that the number of significant characters is divisible by 6, nor would it be advisable to use blanks, which might have an unintended significance. Hence, octal 77, with no Hollerith equivalent, is set aside to serve as a filler. To illustrate use of the filler, if a segment of text should require 63 characters for recording on tape, there would be 10 groups of 6 characters each, then one group of 3 characters plus 3 fillers.

3. Organized Files of Text

The user of a file of text on tape will sometimes take the largest available quantity and handle all of it uniformly, collecting, without regard to source, all the instances of a phenomenon that interests him. For other purposes, he will need to discriminate in some way; he may choose to examine only introductory paragraphs in scientific articles or only articles on a certain subject or only dialogue in plays and novels or only titles. To serve him well, text files must be organized and labeled. In Sec. 2 we described the tape representation of unorganized units of text, for example, printed lines; here we go on to the representation of organizational features—conventions for assembly of many lines of text in a Chinese-box arrangement that we call *catalog format*.

Instead of proposing special formats only for text, we apply conventions that are equally appropriate for dictionaries, grammars, and other sorts of material. We thus save the cost of writing many primitive computer programs to synthesize and analyze statements about form; independent of the substance of the catalog, such programs deal *only* with form. If it were necessary to write new programs for files of different materials, we would be tempted to simplify the organization of each file. Since the catalog formats can be used for every file, we feel free to elaborate the organization of each file as far as is profitable.

3.1. Maps

A catalog is a collection of *data.* Each datum can be large or small, but the datum is the smallest manipulable unit for the programs that operate on catalogs as catalogs; the content of the data is the substance of the catalog. In a text file, most data contain representations of text in the code given in Sec. 2; these data are called *text entries* and each can usually be assumed to contain a line of text. The organization of the file is accomplished by data called *labels,* each marking a significant group of entries. These labels are nested at four levels: (1) a collection of entries is called a *section* and labeled; (2) a labeled collection of sections is a *division*; (3) a *corpus* label is applied to a collection of divisions; (4) a *text file* is a sequence of corpora and has no label. Any entry or labeled group of entries can be annotated in *description* data.

The catalog-management system uses a *tree* diagram to specify the form of a catalog. In Fig. 1 is the tree diagram for text. At its origin is the label for a corpus (CL = corpus label). Under this node, on the second

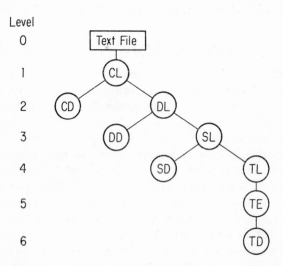

Fig. 1. Map of a text file in catalog format (see text for explanation of symbols).

level, are two *data-class names,* CD = corpus description and DL = division label. In these remarkable *maps,* a single data-class name stands for an unlimited number of data of the named class, just as if one airport on a map of the world could stand for all the world's airports. This simplification, which enables us to draw one map for all catalogs of text before even the first is constructed, is feasible because the catalog-management system imposes enough conventions to guarantee that every datum can be found when the map is followed.

To complete our inspection of Fig. 1, let us use the map as a guide to the preparation of a magnetic tape. We can record only one thing at a time as the tape unrolls; we use the map to decide what datum to take at each step. Starting at the top, we record a côrpus label. Next we go to Level 2 and begin at the left with a corpus description; if several data of this class are to be recorded, we take them one after another. When all description data for the corpus are on the tape, we move to the next node on the same level, which in this map is a division label. We record the first division label for the corpus; perhaps we intend to record several divisions, each with a label, but we must take everything in the first division, that is, data of all classes named under the DL node in the map, before recording a label for the second division. Thus the map requires that when we have recorded the first division label we move at once to Level 3 and record division descriptions (DD). Since there are no nodes under DD, we take as many data of this class as we require and then proceed across Level 3 to node SL. Recording the first section label, we move down to Level 4 and record our first text label (TL), down to Level 5 for a text entry (TE), and down to Level 6 for a text description (TD).

Now we are at the bottom of the map. The next datum to be recorded is another text description for the same entry, if any; otherwise, another text entry with its text descriptions under the same text label; otherwise, the next text label within the section. When the last text label in a section has been recorded, followed by its text entries and their descriptions, another section label goes on the tape. What follows the second and each subsequent section label is just like the material following the first with, of course, no restriction on the number of text labels in any section. When everything pertaining to the last section in a division has been recorded, a new division is begun with its label, description data, and so on. When everything pertaining to the last division is on the tape, a new corpus is begun. The end of the last corpus is the end of the catalog.

In Fig. 2 we present an expanded map with one node for each datum and a diagram descriptive of material entered on a corresponding hypothetical tape. The figure is to be read like a diagram of syntactic dependencies; each node governs those on the level just below and connected

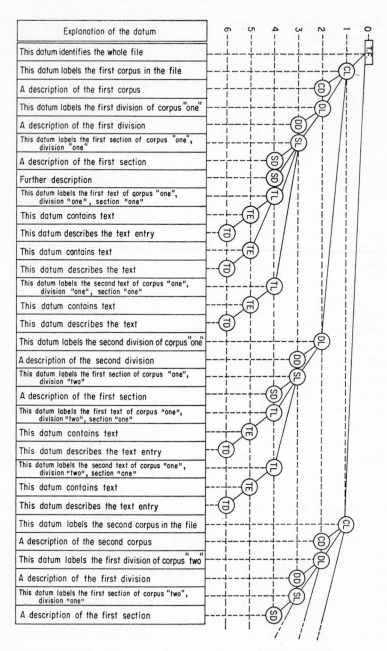

Fig. 2. The tree structure of a sample catalog.

to it, and each node is associated with a segment of the tape diagram by a dotted line.

The main outlines of the map for text files are obvious. A corpus is an enormous block of text, for example, all the Russian text prepared for machine processing at RAND is recorded as one corpus. A division in this corpus corresponds to an issue of a journal, to a book, or to some similar publication unit. Each section is an article or chapter. Descriptions are optional and contain whatever information a particular user feels to be necessary. The description of a corpus can tell in what language it is written, what center produced it, and any other information which would be useful at this size level. The description of a division can specify a scientific discipline, give bibliographic information, and the like. The description of a section can include, for example, the page numbers of the original publication. Text labels are used to differentiate titles, subtitles, authors, summaries, footnotes, body, and the like. They also identify page and line in a way that makes checking the source convenient. Text descriptions, on the other hand, are used for annotation of a freer kind. The map shows that several entry data can follow a text label; this device permits recording of interlinear texts, in which the first entry under a label contains an original-language line; the second, a translation; and so on. Since text descriptions are connected to text entries, not to text labels, the original-language line can be described in one datum and the translation, in another.

The catalog-management system permits null data. Although the map shows a text-description datum under each text entry, this facility would not be equally convenient for all users of the format. It would be wasteful to require every user to insert descriptions, wanted or not, for the sake of those whose text must be described. A null datum occupies no space on tape; it need not be mentioned during preparation of a tape file, and it does not appear when the file is consulted. Thanks to this technique, programs for manipulation of text need not be altered when descriptions are added or deleted; descriptions can be added to any file without alteration of the map (which is the same for every text file) or conversion of programs; and a library containing some text with descriptions and some without can be scanned from end to end without special attention to this variation.

Data of any class can be left null. For example, it would be possible to record data for several divisions within a single corpus without recording any division labels; the results might be bad, but the boundaries between divisions would be discernible nevertheless.

3.2. The Data of a Text File

Form and content are clearly distinguished by the catalog-management system.

Each *text entry* is a string of characters, encoded in accordance with the rules of Sec. 2. Since each entry is independent of all others, each must begin with a flag character.

Description data of all types are encoded as text; Sec. 2 applies to them also. It is thus possible to write descriptions with all the elegance of the printer's art while at the same time a single complex of programs will suffice for the decoding of all data in a text file.

The labels are written with Hollerith characters in restricted formats. Let us take them class by class.

Corpus Labels. Each datum in this class consists of 72 characters. The first 24 constitute a corpus name; the remainder are for notes. As many of these characters as desired can be left blank (not null!). If descriptions are for scholarly use, notes within labels are for use by programmers and librarians. Here the manager of a text file can indicate what corrections have been made to a corpus, what special procedures have been applied, and the like.

Division Labels. The length of the datum is again 72 characters, but only two are allowed for the name of the division, all the rest being given over to notes. The purpose of the restriction on name length is to encourage a brevity that will be gratifying to all who must write division names repeatedly in instructions for correction, scanning, or analysis of text. The notes can be used for an expanded version of the name or for librarian's records.

Section Labels. The same format is used as for the division labels, and with the same argument.

Text Labels. It is intended that a text label be written for each line of original printed text. Since a file will contain a great many text labels, the length of each is limited to six characters. The first character is a type symbol, the remainder is an entry name. The type symbols, listed in Table 8, are redundant in a certain sense; they could presumably be reconstructed

Table 8. Text Type Symbols

T — Title	A — Author
D — Summary	E — Editor's Note
S — Major Section Heading	I — Intermediate Section Heading
M — Minor Section Heading	B — Body
N — Footnote	L — Bibliography ("Literature")
F — Stage Direction	P — Speaker (Drama)

from the spaces and shift symbols contained within the entry. Since the program for the reconstruction job would be complex, and since users may often want to exclude titles, authors' names, and so on, from a search, the redundant symbols have been inserted.

The entry name included in the text label is large in order to permit organization below the level of the section. For example, the five characters can be used for page number and line number or for scene and line number or in whatever manner is natural to the text being recorded.

4 A High-Speed Large-Capacity Dictionary System

Sydney M. Lamb and William H. Jacobsen, Jr.

Editor's Comment: This paper has been abridged by elimination of details concerning either Russian or the IBM 704. The linguistic detail, strengthening the argument that a high degree of compression can be achieved, and the programming detail, demonstrating how ingenuity can produce a fast program without requiring an excessive amount of storage, are of less interest than the broad outlines of the authors' system.

1. Introduction

This paper describes a method of adapting dictionaries for use by a computer in such a way that comprehensiveness of vocabulary coverage can be maximized while look-up time is minimized. Although the programming of the system has not yet been completed, it is estimated at the time of writing that it will allow for a dictionary of 20,000 entries or more, with a total look-up time of about 8 milliseconds (0.008 seconds) per word, when used on an IBM 704 computer with 32,000 words of core storage. With a proper system of segmentation, a dictionary of 20,000 entries can handle several hundred thousand different words, thus providing ample coverage for a single fairly broad field of science. Although the system has been designed specifically for purposes of machine translation of Russian, it is applicable to other areas of linguistic data processing in which dictionaries are needed.

2. Preliminary Definitions

An entity for which there is (or should be) a dictionary entry is a lexical item or *lex*. A text is made up of a sequence of lexes, for each of which we hope to find a dictionary entry, if we are translating or analyzing it.

Note: This work was performed at the University of California, Berkeley, with the support of the National Science Foundation. Reprinted from *Mechanical Translation,* Vol. 6 (November 1961), pp. 76–107, with the permission of authors and publisher.

It is also made up of a sequence of words, but if any segmentation of words is incorporated in the system, many of the words will consist of more than one lex. (In the system used at the University of California, there are about two lexes per word, on the average.) A *word,* on the graphemic level, is a sequence of graphemes which can occur between spaces; any specific occurrence of a word is a *word token.* A lex (in the present discussion) has its existence on the graphemic level, and corresponds to a *lexeme* on the morphemic level. Any specific occurrence of a lex is a *lex token.* The relationship between lex and lexeme is like that between morph and morpheme: that is, a lexeme may have more than one graphemic representation, or lex (since one or more of its constituent morphemes has more than one morph). Such alternate representations may be called *allolexes* of the lexeme. Just as a (graphemic) word may comprise more than one lex, so a lex may comprise more than one morph.

A dictionary entry may be thought of as consisting of two parts, the *heading* and the *exposition.** The heading is an instance (or coded representation) of the lex itself, and serves to identify the entry. The remainder of the entry, the exposition, is the information which is provided concerning that lex. If the dictionary is part of an automatic translation system, the exposition might contain the following three parts (not necessarily separated): (1) the syntactic-semantic code, signifying distributional and semantic properties about which information may be needed in dealing with other lexemes occurring in the environment of the one in question; (2) (highly compressed) instructions for selecting the appropriate target representation for any given environment; and (3) the target representations. In an efficient automatic dictionary system the target representations might be kept together on tape, to be brought into core storage as a body when needed, after the look-up and translation proper have been completed. In this case, the expositions would be split up, the target representations being separated from the rest; in their place would be put the addresses where the representations would be located after the "target-language tape" has been run into core storage. Then we have what may be called *abbreviated expositions.†*

---

* These terms correspond (more or less) to *argument* and *function* in William S. Cooper, "The Storage Problem," *Mechanical Translation* 5.74-83 (1958). (Although the authors favor the principle of priority in nomenclature, they felt it necessary to introduce these new items since Cooper's *argument* applies ambiguously to both *heading* and *vestigand,* which can be quite different.) The authors have profited not only from this article, but also from several informal discussions with Mr. Cooper.

† The next stage of refinement would be to split many of the target forms into parts which recur in other target forms. This would require using more than one address in the abbreviated exposition for many forms, but it enables simplification of many translation instructions, as well as a considerable shortening of the target language tape.

Where a lexeme has allolexes, there must be a heading for each allolex, but (except for that part of the syntactic code which defines their complementary distribution) they all have the same exposition. The exposition, then (aside from the qualification mentioned parenthetically above), is oriented to the morphemic level, while the headings are graphemic in character. In a dictionary, the exposition for such a lexeme could be repeated under each allolex, or all but one of the allolexes could have *cross-referential expositions,* which would refer to the full exposition given for that one allolex.

A word being looked up in the dictionary, or ready to be looked up, may be called the *vestigand* (based on the gerundive of Lat. vestigare, "to track, trace out; to search after, seek out; to inquire into, investigate"; hence, "that which is to be traced out, searched after, investigated"). A vestigand will coincide with some heading only in the special case in which it is not segmented; otherwise it will contain two or more headings. The look-up process involves segmentation as well as location of headings. (An alternative approach has been used* in which "suffixes" are separated before the look-up process begins. Such a practice is rejected here, since it (1) often leads to false segmentation; (2) requires the use of arbitrary, non-structural segmentation principles; (3) involves setting up more stem allolexes, hence more dictionary entries, than would otherwise be necessary.) Every word token in a text is a vestigand at the time it is being looked up.

3. Simple System

Let us begin considering the dictionary problem in terms of the simplest type of organization, in which the machine dictionary is set up very much like an ordinary printed dictionary, except that stems themselves are used as headings, rather than combinations of the stems with standard suffixes such as nominative singular or infinitive. In the simple system, then, there is a list of entries, each one containing its heading, followed by the exposition. For this type of dictionary, the look-up process would involve matching the vestigand or part of it with one of the headings, after which the exposition next to this heading would be placed where needed for further reference after the process of look-up has been completed. (We assume for any type of machine dictionary system that the look-up process is handled for all of the words in the text or some portion thereof before the next stage of translation begins. This sequence of operations has apparently

---

* See, for example, A. G. Oettinger, W. Foust, V. Giuliano, K. Magassy, and L. Matejka, *Linguistic and Machine Methods for Compiling and Updating the Harvard Automatic Dictionary,* Preprints of Papers for the International Conference on Scientific Information, Area 5, 137-159 (1958), especially p. 141.

been universally recognized as essential for translation by computers, because of the limitation in the size of rapid-access memories.)

In this type of organization the dictionary is set up much like dictionaries that are used by human beings, except for the obvious adaptations needed for storage in the machine—such as the use of binary coding, etc.

The reason we have a problem is that in any of the available computers there is insufficient space to provide for the whole dictionary within the rapid access memory. The usual solution has been the "Batch Method,"* in which each "batch" of words (i.e., all the word tokens in a portion of text) is alphabetized before the look-up proper begins. The dictionary is stored on magnetic tape and is organized by alphabetic order of the headings like familiar paper dictionaries. In the look-up process, it is brought into core storage a portion at a time, and all the words in the alphabetized batch are looked up in one pass of the tape. As headings are matched, the adjoining expositions are stored in some specified location still in alphabetic order of the corresponding headings. Having obtained the expositions for all the lexical items in the batch, the machine must re-sort them back into text order. Thus there are two areas of nonproductive data processing: sorting the vestigands into alphabetic order and sorting the expositions back into text order. If this excess baggage could be done away with, a great saving of time would result.

4. Segregating the Headings

We have already noted that it might be efficient to divide each exposition into its target representations and an abbreviated exposition, keeping all the target representations together in one body until needed. The amount of time that can be reclaimed by such separation depends to a great extent on various features of the translation system itself. In any case, a much more significant saving of time will result if an additional separation is effected. We may detach the headings from the (abbreviated or full) expositions and then combine the headings into one body and the expositions into another.

This principle has already been implemented in a look-up system de-

---

* Previously described (with the term *batch*) by Victor H. Yngve, "The Technical Feasibility of Translating Languages by Machine," *Electrical Engineering* 75.994-999 (1956), p. 996. This method has been used by MT groups at Georgetown University, Ramo-Wooldridge, and Harvard. See A. F. R. Brown, *Manual for a "Simulated Linguistic Computer"—A System for Direct Coding of Machine Translation,* Georgetown University, Occasional Papers on Machine Translation No. 1, Washington, D.C. (1959), p. 36; *Experimental Machine Translation of Russian to English,* Ramo-Wooldridge Division of Thompson Ramo Wooldridge Inc., Project Progress Report M20-8U13, Los Angeles (1958), p. 26; and P. E. Jones, Jr., *The Continuous Dictionary Run,* Mathematical Linguistics and Automatic Translation, Report No. NSF-2, Sec. I, Harvard Computation Laboratory (1959), pp. 11–18.

signed at The RAND Corporation.* The body of expositions, which we may call the *exposition list* for short, is kept on magnetic tape until after the essential part of the look-up process has been completed. The economy involved in terms of space saving for the look-up itself is obvious. The location of a given dictionary entry requires that only the heading part of the entry be known. And for dictionaries of up to several thousand entries, it is possible to store all the headings within a 32,000 word rapid access memory. At the end of the look-up process, the machine has for each lex token an address for the exposition to which it corresponds.

Now, for a dictionary of adequate size, the exposition list itself is much too large to be in core storage at one time; it may comprise about 70 to 90 percent of the volume of the dictionary as a whole. On the other hand, a 32,000 word memory can contain the expositions for all the different lexes occurring in any one text, provided it is of reasonable length. The RAND group has found that while a typical issue of a journal contains around 30,000 word tokens, there are never more than 3,000 different lexical items represented in it, where by lexical items we mean the type of units used in the RAND system. (The degree of segmentation for that system is less than that which has been worked out at the University of California. Therefore, the corresponding figure would be less than 3,000 for the "Berkeley system.") Abbreviated expositions for all those 3,000 dictionary entries can be contained in core storage at one time, since an estimate of eight machine words as the average size of an abbreviated exposition is liberal.† This means that an added feature is necessary which will make it possible to bring into core storage for the stage of translation proper only those two or three thousand expositions which are actually needed. There are several ways of making this possible, one of which is included in the RAND system. A somewhat different process is incorporated in the present scheme. We may call it the *intermediate stage.*

As each of the headings is located, what will be found is neither the exposition itself nor the address where the exposition will be stored. It is,

---

* But not yet programmed. The system was designed by Hugh Kelly and Theodore Ziehe of the RAND programming staff, but programming of it has been suspended during a test of the feasibility of an alternative system which makes use of a RAMAC. Information concerning the system was obtained from personal communication. Another system designed by Mr. Ziehe which also uses the principle of segregating headings is described by him in "Glossary Look-up Made Easy," *Proceedings of the National Symposium on Machine Translation,* Prentice-Hall, Inc., Englewood Cliffs, N.J. (1961), pp. 325-334. The idea of heading segregation has been mentioned previously in print by William S. Cooper, "The Storage Problem," p. 75.

† For the purposes of this paper, a machine word consists of 36 bits. An abbreviated exposition of more than average complexity might have a syntactic-semantic code of three machine words, three machine words of compressed instructions, and two machine words of target-form addresses.

instead, what we may call the *intermediate address*. After the headings for the text have been identified, in place of the original text there will be arranged in text sequence a series of these intermediate addresses, one for each lex token. Then about twenty thousand words of core storage are to be filled from tape (in one file) with what we may call the *intermediate list*. Each machine word of the intermediate list represents a particular dictionary entry, and each intermediate address is the address of the corresponding word in the intermediate list. The use of the intermediate list is explained below (see *The Intermediate Stage*).

When the intermediate stage has been completed, only the expositions which are actually needed are left in core storage, and they are all immediately addressable during the stage of translation proper.

5. Addressing the Dictionary Entry

If core storage were large enough that we could use the shape of the heading itself as an address, only the intermediate address would have to be stored, and the heading, rather than occupying storage space, would be the address of the location where the intermediate address would be stored. Obviously, there is no core storage large enough for this method. Moreover, if there were, its use for this purpose would be a colossal extravagance. Let us consider, however, some of the more realistic aspects of this general idea. Suppose we were to take just the first two letters of the vestigand and use them as an address. If the standard 6-bit code is used, the table needed would require 4,096 (2^{12}) machine words. Even to use this device with no further refinements gives a rather efficient system for as much as it covers. That is, if we get the desired location narrowed down according to the first two letters, we have already come very close to it, and we have spent practically no time at all.

We have saved some space as well. Suppose the dictionary has 18,000 entries. Then the space required to store the first two letters of each heading would be the equivalent of 6,000 machine words. But our table occupies only 4,096 words, so we have a space saving of almost 2,000 words.

Below there are introduced a series of refinements which make it possible to efficiently use a portion of each vestigand as an address. Space limitations require that the process be somewhat indirect; nevertheless, the system provides extremely rapid entry into a dictionary.

First of all we shall see that it is necessary to conduct the addressing letter by letter. This principle is, in fact, the key to the system.* It enables us to take advantage of the fact that letters tend to occur in certain com-

---

* An application of this principle similar to the one given here is described by Rene De La Briandais, File Searching Using Variable Length Keys, *Proceedings of the Western Joint Computer Conference*, (1959), pp. 295–298. His system differs from ours primarily in that each successive table is scanned entry by entry to

binations, and that many "theoretically possible" combinations of letters do not occur in natural written languages. It also permits a simple and direct approach to segmentation. In conducting the look-up operation, we may use the first letter of the vestigand as an address in the "first-letter table," a table of sixty-four words (if the standard 6-bit code is used). At this address is given the final address of the table to consult for the next letter.* At the location corresponding to each possible first character, there is an address which gives the location of the table for the second. The second letter of the vestigand may now be placed in an index register, and the proper address for the third-letter table may be obtained by addressing.

For the first letter we need sixty-four positions in the table, and for the second we would need sixty-four tables of sixty-four words each—if the language of the text used sixty-four characters any of which could occur initially. But in fact we do not need this many. For the second letter we need only as many tables as there occur first letters. If we are using an IBM 704 computer, only forty-eight characters are readily available (the letters of the alphabet, ten digits, and various other symbols); if we limit ourselves to these, then for the second character we will need forty-eight tables of sixty-four entries each, occupying 3,072 machine words. (We must allow space for an entire block of sixty-four entries per table in order to provide insurance against the possibility of an error.)

Instead of visualizing a set of forty-eight second-letter tables and a first-letter table, one may prefer to think of an array containing forty-eight rows and sixty-four columns, in which the row we get represents the first letter of the word and the position we get on it represents the second letter.

When we get to the third letter, the economy of letter by letter addressing becomes more striking, as we need only a few hundred tables, very much less than the 4,096 (64 × 64) which would be necessary for direct addressing taking the first three letters together. The number of tables needed for the third character (if this technique is used for the third character of all vestigands) is equal to the number of occurring combinations of first two characters which can be followed by a third character, i.e., there must be a third-letter table for each such combination. If all possible combina-

---

determine whether the next letter is entered, instead of being directly addressed with the next letter as an index. The use of this alternative type of letter table as an intermediate step between the directly addressable letter tables and the truncate lists would be a device for conserving space so as to allow more headings to be accommodated, at a cost of greater look-up time and more red tape. For this purpose, the tables should probably be arranged so that the entries in a given table occupy successive machine words, rather than being in the overlapping arrangement described in this reference, which is more applicable to situations in which the tables are to be repeatedly formed anew.

* We refer here and in what follows specifically to the IBM 704, in which index registers are subtractive.

tions of the forty-eight available characters occurred as first and second letter, the number of tables needed would be 2,304 (48 $\times$ 48), but of course most of these combinations do not occur. Further details are given below under the heading *Space Needs for Letter Tables*.

It is of course necessary to conserve further space. The need becomes particularly clear when we realize that there are over 3,000 occurring combinations of first three letters. There are two possible approaches to reducing space needs, both of which must be used: (1) the adoption of refinements to cut down the size of the tables; (2) the elimination of the use of these tables in certain situations.

6. Code Conversion

A possibility for reducing the size of the tables is suggested by the fact that there are for most languages thirty-two letters or less in the alphabet, whereas there are sixty-four entries needed in a table if the usual 6-bit code is used. (The number of entries in a table of this type is, of course, 2^n, where n is the number of bits in the code.) Thirty-two characters can be handled by a 5-bit code, and the number of entries needed in a table would be only thirty-two. Thus we can cut the space requirements by half.

Naturally, some provision must be made for nonalphabetic characters. There are various ways of managing this. In a language with twenty-six letters like English, there are six extra spaces within the thirty-two for the common non-alphabetic symbols such as blank, comma, period, semicolon, etc. The Russian alphabet seems less tractable at first glance, since it has thirty-two letters. Two of these letters are, however, in complementary distribution so that only one symbol is needed for both of them, and an efficient coding system would use only one symbol for both, no matter what type of dictionary organization is used. These letters are the soft sign, which occurs only after consonants, and the short "i," which occurs only after vowels. In the transliteration system used at the University of California, both of these letters are represented by *j*. The transliterated alphabet, then, has only thirty-one letters. The thirty-second position in the table may be used for "nothing" (i.e., end of a heading); its contents will be the intermediate address for a heading ending at that point, rather than the address of another table.

Space in tables need not be provided for the nonalphabetic characters, since they require special treatment. For example, in the case of arabic numbers, we will not want to look up the whole number since we will not want to have all the arabic numbers in the dictionary. Instead, whenever an arabic number comes up, it will be handled character by character, and no translation will be necessary since each character will be the same in the target language as in the input text. Thus the computer will not proceed in the same way for the special symbols as for the letters, and it will not need letter tables for them.

The machine can convert from the standard BCD to a code in which the thirty-one letters have a zero in the first bit and all the other characters (punctuation marks, numerals, etc.) have a one in the first bit. We still have a 6-bit code, but it can be used to give an effective 5-bit code. Suppose we place the first bit in the sign bit position of the machine word; the other five bits can be placed in the low-order positions of the same machine word. This makes it easy to check whether the next character is alphabetic or not, and after the checking, we have in effect a 5-bit code, making possible a table of only thirty-two entries.

7. Two Table Entries per Machine Word

Let us at first consider this refinement independently of the previous one. It is another means of cutting down the length of the tables from sixty-four to thirty-two words. Since the table entries consist only of addresses, we may economize by placing two of them in each machine word.

The next step is to combine the two refinements, with the result that only sixteen cells are needed for each table. Then the tables have thirty-two entries, two of them in each word, and accommodate only the letters.

8. Space Needs for Letter Tables

As indicated above, our space needs for the letter tables can be calculated with reference only to the alphabetic characters, of which there are thirty-one (contrasting ones) in Russian. For the first letter we need one table, and we need one second-letter table for each possible first letter. Three of the Russian letters (й/ь ъ ы) do not occur initially, so twenty-eight second-letter tables are needed. Thus, at sixteen machine words per second-letter table, roughly 500 words of memory space will be occupied by the tables for the first and second letters. Note that the equivalent of over 6,000 machine words would be needed to store the first two letters of 20,000 headings.

If the letter tables are used for the third letter of all vestigands, the number of tables needed is equal to the number of possible combinations of first two letters, minus those combinations for which no third letter is possible. An estimate of this number may be obtained by tabulating the possibilities for all of the words in some appropriate dictionary. Table 1 shows all the possibilities for the first two letters occurring in Callaham's

Table 1. Combinations of First Two and First Three Letters
(Based on Callaham)

+ one of the possible third characters is a break
– one of the possible third characters is a period
* a prefix of two letters
T number of possible second letters

Chemical and Technical Dictionary.* Every square occupied by a number represents an occurring combination of first two letters. The number in each such square indicates how many possible third characters may follow, including period (in the case of abbreviations) and blank (or other punc-

---

* Ludmilla Ignatiev Callaham, *Russian-English Technical and Chemical Dictionary*, New York and London (1947). Table 1 was prepared by Janet V. Kemp and Alfred B. Hudson.

tuation, counted as one). An asterisk in a square betokens a prefix, implying that there may be additional possible third letters. The numbers in the column labeled T indicate how many second letters can follow each first letter. (In making the tabulation, capitalization of letters was ignored.) The table discloses 507 occurring combinations of first two letters (out of a "theoretically possible" 961), twenty of which do not occur with any following third letter. This result would indicate a need for 487 third-letter tables. With regard to this figure it should be noted that the Callaham dictionary is somewhat larger than the one envisaged in this paper, since the former, by a rough estimate, contains some 33,000 entries. To be sure, many of these entries would not be represented as distinct entries in the planned system because of segmentation, but the effect of the segmentation is partially offset by the fact that many of the Callaham entries cover multiple lexemes. At any rate one may say that the Callaham dictionary probably accommodates a few thousand more lexemes than the twenty thousand to which the present discussion applies.

Table 1 also provides an estimate, albeit somewhat high, of the number of combinations of first three letters which can be expected. The number of such combinations occurring in Callaham (equal to the total of all the numbers in the squares less one for each $+$ or $-$) is 3,440. A number of these, of course, cannot be followed by any fourth letter, since they constitute lexes and are not included in larger lexes. Allowing for this factor and for the larger size of the Callaham dictionary, we are still left with perhaps well over 2,000 as the number of fourth-letter tables which would be needed if the tables were to be used for the fourth letter of all vestigands. At sixteen words per table, this would amount to over 32,000 words, obviously too much space to allow. Aside from the fact that the limits of the capacity of core storage would be exceeded, it would be a highly inefficient utilization of space since the great preponderance of the table entries would be empty (reflecting lack of occurrence of the letter sequences involved).

There are devices available which could cut down the size of the tables to eight words each, or even to less than that, at the expense of an appreciable amount of look-up time. However, any kind of letter by letter addressing or searching is necessarily inefficient after a certain point, just as searching through a list of headings for a match is inefficient up to that point. In other words, the letter by letter addressing should be continued until the possibilities for the desired heading have been narrowed down to a very few, at which point it becomes more efficient to consider up to several following letters at the same time.

Table 2, which is based on Table 1, shows the high proportion of combinations of first two letters for which there are only a very limited number of possibilities for the third letter. For about a quarter of the two-letter

Table 2. Number of Combinations of First Two Letters for Which There Are Very Few Possibilities for the Third Letter (for Russian, First Letter a Through o; Data from Table 1)

First Letter	Total Number of Different Possible 2nd Letters	Number of Different Possible 2nd Letters for which the Number of Possible Third Letters is only:				
		1 or 0	2 or less	3 or less	4 or less	5 or less
а	26	4	7	9	10	10
б	13	1	4	4	4	4
в	29	4	7	9	12	13
г	20	8	10	10	11	12
д	20	5	7	10	10	12
е	18	8	12	13	15	16
ж	17	9	10	12	12	13
з	14	1	6	6	9	10
и	23	6	7	10	10	12
й/ь	0	0	0	0	0	0
к	20	5	8	9	10	10
л	18	8	9	10	10	10
м	21	5	7	11	12	12
н	12	4	5	7	7	7
о	25	3	5	7	8	10
	276	71	104	127	140	151
% of 276:		26%	38%	46%	51%	55%

combinations, there is at most one possibility for the third letter. For well over a third of them there are only two possibilities or less, and for over half of them there are less than five possibilities.

As is to be expected, the corresponding proportions are even higher for limited fourth letter possibilities after combinations of first three letters.

It will conserve time as well as space if the system is designed so that in the look-up process, beginning with the third letter, a test is made to determine whether to continue to another letter table or to proceed to the next stage of the process, in which one of the few headings remaining as possibilities can be selected.

9. The Truncate Lists

After the stage of letter by letter addressing for each vestigand we have what may be called the *truncated vestigand*, all or part of which will have to be matched with some truncated heading, or *truncate*. It is estimated that a typical system will have some three or four thousand *truncate lists* containing on the average five or six truncates each. In each of these lists the truncates will be portions of headings all of which begin with the same first three or four letters or so. The truncates of each list can be listed in order of length, from longest to shortest, and in reverse alphabetical (i.e., numerical) order wherever two or more have the same length. The look-up routine at this stage involves simply going through the truncate list from the beginning to get a match, either with the entire truncated vestigand or the first few letters thereof. In the latter case the remainder is to be looked up in the suffix tables.

It is necessary to mark a boundary between adjacent truncate lists, and this can be done by placing a minus in the sign bit of the first machine word of each. Five bits are needed for the segmentation-checking code, whose use is explained below (see *Segmentation*). This leaves thirty positions for the truncate itself, thus providing for five BCD characters. For those truncates which are longer than five characters, the following cell (or two) may be used. If an effective segmentation system is used, the number of headings for which a second supplementary word is needed is very small. (For the dictionary being compiled at the University of California, a preliminary survey indicates that two supplementary words will be required by less than one per cent of the truncates.)

If, upon comparison, a truncated vestigand is found to be numerically smaller than a given truncate (except the first one in the list, which has a minus sign), comparison can immediately be made with the following truncate. If, on the other hand, it is numerically larger, it is immediately obvious, as it were, that it cannot be matched with any truncate in the list and must therefore be shortened by at least one letter before further comparison can hope to be fruitful.

It is not necessary to provide space for the storage of intermediate addresses of headings located during this stage, since their intermediate addresses can be identical with those of the cells where their truncates (or final portions thereof) are stored.

10. Segmentation

Much of the power of the system described here resides in the simple means it provides for segmenting words into ideal units for purposes of translation. This ability to segment effectively not only promotes efficiency in the translation routines; it also enables the automatic translator to deal with most neologisms and, by the same token, allows it to accommodate a vocabulary of hundreds of thousands of graphemic words, even though there are only twenty thousand dictionary entries.

Operational segmentation of words by the machine program can be effective, in the sense that it can follow the same principles of segmentation that would be used in a structural description,* if the program is so constructed that it takes the longest heading contained in the vestigand (beginning at the left) as the first lex, the longest heading contained in the *remainder* (if any) as the next, etc., provided that the resulting tentative segmentation yields lexes whose co-occurrence in the order found is allowable. The proviso makes it necessary that *segmentation codes* for all headings be present at the time of look-up. The codes can be used to test the compatibility of provisional segments, and such testing must include a check to determine whether the final (or only) provisional segment can occur without a following lex. The first lex of a polylexemic vestigand will be either a base or a prefix. If it is the former, then the suffix tables will be used in continuing the look-up process; if it is a prefix, the main part of the look-up system will be used. However, if the initial segment is a base and no provisional segmentation checks out using the suffix tables for the remainder, the word could be a compound and the remainder can be looked up in the main part of the system. For Russian, this roundabout treatment of compounds can be avoided for the most part by including known and/or frequently-occurring compounds in the dictionary as unit lexes. The roundabout procedure would then be used only for infrequent and/or neologistic compounds. On the other hand, for languages in which compounding is a highly productive process, like German, such treatment is undesirable since it would make the dictionary too bulky. Overall efficiency might be maximized for German by including suffixes in the main part of the dictionary, so that all remainders could be looked up in the same manner.

For those headings which end in the truncate lists (rather than the letter tables) the requirement that the longest contained heading be chosen is built into the system as an automatic feature, since the truncates are listed in reverse order of length (i.e., from longest to shortest). If segmentation checking fails to yield a satisfactory result, consideration can pass immediately to the following truncate in the list.

On the other hand, many headings are short enough to come to an end while the look-up process is still in the letter tables. Of these, some are included within longer headings while others are not. The latter are auto-

---

* Except with regard to the degree of segmentation. While the ultimate constituents on the morphemic level for a structural description are the morphemes, segmentation for a translation system should stop short of this point. It is not efficient to segment, with regard to a given construction, if the target representations of the constitutes cannot economically be treated as combinations of the representations of the constituents. In addition, segmentation of individual forms should generally be avoided whenever the cut would necessitate the setting up of allolexes that would otherwise be unnecessary.

matically provided for in the program by a feature to be described below. In the case of the former, the look-up routine will need to know, as it were, whether one of the longer headings is also contained in the vestigand, so it will have to continue the look-up process, usually by going to a truncate list. If it does not find a longer contained heading, however, it will want to return to the shorter one. Provision for such return can be furnished by keeping track of the segmentation code and intermediate address of each such heading as the look-up routine proceeds. For each vestigand then (except those not composed of letters), we will want to make a short *segmentation checking list*.

Figure 1 shows the ways in which different combinations of conditions found in the machine lead to different subsequent actions as the nth letter is being looked up. At the head of the four left-hand columns are entered four alternative possibilities having to do with the letter sequence that ends with the nth letter and its relationship to the letter sequences that are entered in the dictionary. Within each column are found descriptions of the actual conditions in the text or letter tables that correspond to one or the other of the alternatives given at its head, each alternative and its corresponding condition being labeled by the same number or letter. In the column at the right are found the actions that are to be taken when the combination of conditions given in each horizontal row is encountered. A blank space in the table indicates that the particular question is irrelevant for determining the course of action, under the combination of conditions defined to its left.

The descriptions of these actions which are entered in the chart must be amplified as follows. Testing the remainder involves determining whether or not it consists of a suffix or combination of suffixes entered in the dictionary. If a positive result is obtained, segmentation checking will reveal whether or not the segmentation codes of the stem and suffix(es) are compatible. When a test of the remainder and segmentation check, either for the longest sequence found to be entered in the dictionary or for shorter ones, is indicated as the action to be taken, and a correct segmentation is obtained, the machine will then store the intermediate addresses of the lexes involved. After every remainder test or segmentation check which yields negative results, there will be a looping back, not shown on the chart, to determine whether there are shorter sequences contained in the vestigand which are entered in the dictionary, and, if so, to test the resulting remainders. If there is no shorter sequence in such a case, the machine will provide a transliteration of the word, together with a mark indicating that it was not found in the dictionary. After the machine has either stored the intermediate addresses of the lexes or transliterated the vestigand, it will begin the look-up of the next word token.

nth letter			$(n+1)$th letter	
I. is not: II. is:	A. is: B. is not:	1. is: 2. is not:	a. is: b. is not:	Situation
last alphabetic character in word	in a sequence entered in dictionary	final letter of a heading	in a sequence entered in dictionary	
$(n+1)$th-letter is:	nth-letter table has:	$(n+1)$th-letter table has:	$(n+1)$th-letter table has:	Action taken
I. alphabetic	A. address for $(n+1)$th-letter table	1. intermed. address and segmentation code	a. address for $(n+2)$th-letter table or list	Store segmentation code: go to table or list for $(n+2)$th letter — 1
			b. no address for $(n+2)$th-letter table or list	Test remainder and check segmentation — 2
		2. no intermed. address or segmentation code	a. address for $(n+2)$th-letter table or list	Go to table or list for $(n+2)$th letter — 3
			b. no address for $(n+2)$th-letter table or list	Try shorter sequence (s) — 4
	B. no address for $(n+1)$th-letter table			Try shorter sequence (s) — 5
II. non-alphabetic	A. address for $(n+1)$th-letter table	1. intermed. address and segmentation code		Check whether sequence occurs without suffix — 6
		2. no intermed. address or segmentation code		Try shorter sequence (s) — 7
	B. no address for $(n+1)$th-letter table			Try shorter sequence (s) — 8

Fig. 1. Status of tables and action taken under each possible situation.

It may be helpful to have examples of three-letter sequences that will fall into the various categories of our chart as the second letter is being looked up. For each category two such sequences are given, one beginning with в, and one with д. Since в is a one-letter lex, while д is not, the sequences beginning with the former letter will contain a shorter sequence whose segmentation may be checked if this becomes necessary, while those beginning with the latter letter will not. The differences between the categories should be clear if it is remembered that во and да are two-letter lexes, while the other two-letter sequences (ве, вф, дф, дн) are not. The examples, then, are: 1, вот, дар; 2, воф, дас; 3, век, дне; 4, вем, днс; 5, вфа дфа; 6, во#, да#; 7, ве#, дн#; 8, вф#, дф#.

11. Segmentation Checking

The fact that a provisional segmentation yields a stem present in the dictionary and a suffix also present does not necessarily mean that the vestigand has been correctly segmented. It is necessary to check whether the provisional suffix can occur with the potential stem from which it has been separated, since the provisional segmentation could be a false one for either of two reasons: (1) the vestigand or one of its constituent lexes is absent from the dictionary and it happens to lend itself to a spurious segmentation; (2) the real base is shorter than the one provisionally selected.

As an example of the first situation, suppose that the form ранет "rennet (a type of apple)" has not found its way into our dictionary, but turns up as a vestigand. Without segmentation checking, it would be identified as consisting of the verb stem ран "to injure" (also a noun stem meaning "wound") plus the third person singular suffix -ет. Segmentation checking can identify such a segmentation as spurious, since ран belongs to that class of verb stems for which the third sg. suffix has the allomorph -ит rather than -ет. With segmentation checking, then, the machine may be made aware, as it were, of the fact that ранет is absent from the dictionary and it can print out a transliteration, together with a mark indicating the absence from the dictionary of the form. The reason for the need to check the segmentation during the look-up process when this type of situation occurs is that it is desirable for the machine to dispense with the Russian graphemic forms after they have been looked up; but any transliteration of forms absent from the dictionary must be done before they are discarded.

The second type of situation, in which the real base is shorter than the one provisionally selected, may be illustrated by the form позволят. The longest contained heading would be позволя "to permit/allow (imperfective)," leaving as the provisional suffix -т, an allomorph of the past passive participial suffix. Segmentation checking will reveal that these two lexes cannot occur with each other. Thus the next longest contained heading, позвол, "to permit/allow (perfective)" will be tried, and since the suffix, -ят "third person plural non-past," will be shown to be compatible with the stem, this segmentation will be selected as the correct one.

The checking can be accomplished by means of a table in core storage which can be thought of as a matrix in which the rows represent suffix classes (most of which will contain a single member), the columns base classes distinguished on the basis of occurrence with the suffixes. Each of the elements of the matrix will consist of a single bit with the value zero or one depending upon whether or not the combination represented is allowable.

According to the design of the system described above, 5 bits are allowed in each machine word of the truncate lists and in each final word of the letter tables for the segmentation code. One of the 32 possible combinations is needed for long truncates as an indication that the truncate continues in the following word. Thus we are allowed 31 different segmentation codes, probably enough for all practical purposes, even though this amount is clearly insufficient to reflect all the details of an exhaustive classification.* Using this number of segmentation codes, each row of the matrix can be stored in a single cell.

12. The Intermediate Stage

After the look-up and segmentation checking stages, we will have recorded on tape a list of addresses, one for each lex token of the original text, arranged in the same order as that in which the lexes occur in the text. Since the segmentation system used at the University of California gives about twice as many lex tokens as word tokens in a text, an initial text of 30,000 words would now be represented by a list of about 60,000 addresses.

It may be helpful in following the explanations in this section to refer to Fig. 2, which is a block diagram of the translation process, showing the points at which information is transferred between tapes and core storage. Our discussion so far has been concerned with the operations in the second

---

* Minor classes which, if included, would bring the number to more than 31, can be dealt with in one or more of three ways. For a given deviant base we can either (1) refrain from segmenting and enter the composite form as a heading; or (2) assign the deviant base to a class of slightly wider distribution, after ascertaining that no false segmentation is likely to result. But if for some use of the system these two devices prove to be inadequate and it becomes desirable to use more than 31 segmentation codes, (3) additional codes can be assigned to deviant bases and they can be placed in supplementary machine words in the truncate lists. Code 31 would then mean either that the truncate continues in the following cell or that the base is of a deviant type whose code is given in the following cell.

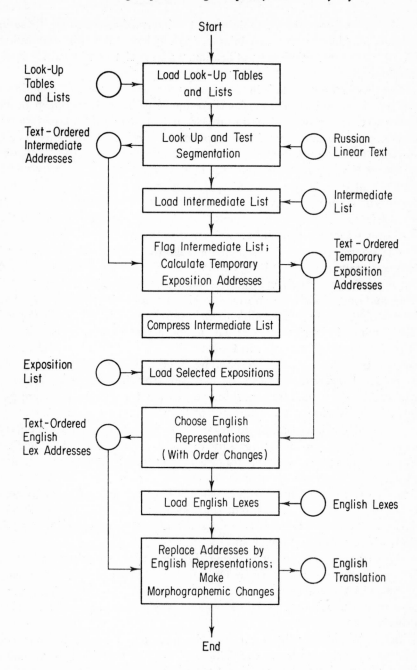

Fig. 2. The translation process.

block, and the operations pertaining to the intermediate stage are those in the next four blocks. The remaining operations have to do with translation proper rather than dictionary utilization, and are not considered in detail in this paper.

Our problem now is to bring into core storage, from the tape containing the actual expositions, the entries corresponding to the lexes which occur in the text being processed, and to replace each text-ordered address by the address to the location that the corresponding exposition will occupy in core storage. This is done by means of an *intermediate list*. The addresses which we have on tape are addresses to this list, and each one may therefore be called an *intermediate address*. Note that the initial stages of look-up give us neither the expositions themselves nor any part thereof (except for the information used in segmentation checking), nor do they yield the addresses where the expositions are stored at that point.

The intermediate list is used in the following manner. It is first read into core storage so that it is located in a block of consecutive words. Then the tape of text-ordered intermediate addresses is read in, a portion at a time, and operations are performed to give the following results: (1) The intermediate word corresponding to each different lex in the text is flagged with a minus in its sign bit. (2) The temporary exposition address is calculated for each different lex in the text. (3) This address is stored in the address portion of each corresponding intermediate word, replacing the exposition length number. (4) Each text-ordered intermediate address is replaced by the temporary exposition address for the lex, and these are put on tape for use during the next stage of translation.

After all the intermediate addresses have been replaced by temporary exposition addresses, it is necessary to make a *compressed intermediate list*. To do this we use a simple routine to run through the intermediate list, pick out the flagged intermediate words, and recopy them into a shorter list. This compressed intermediate list will have a length of as many machine words as there are different lexes in the text, some 2,000 to 3,000. The purpose of making it is to clear space in core storage for the expositions which are to be brought in.

After this we are ready to bring the necessary expositions into core storage from the exposition list. Only the expositions of those dictionary entries which are actually needed are kept in core storage, and they will all remain there, immediately addressable, during the stage of translation proper.

In the intermediate list there must be one entry for each heading (or lex) that is provided for in the dictionary, but the exposition list contains only one entry for each exposition (or lexeme). Thus for those expositions that correspond to more than one heading (i.e., those lexemes that have allolexes), more than one entry in the intermediate list will contain an address to the same entry in the exposition list. The intermediate list, then, is seen to be, among other things, a device for passing from the graphemic level to the morphemic (or lexemic) one. The present system, or any system which stores expositions separately from their headings so that the headings representing the allolexes of a lexeme may all refer to the same exposition, entered only once, will be seen to differ from an ordinary dictionary by having neither cross-referential nor duplicate expositions. It therefore does not choose the heading corresponding to any one of the allolexes as a primary one that would be more directly related to the exposition for the lexeme in question. This type of system is more in accord with modern linguistic theory, which gives equal status to all allomorphs of a morpheme.

There are, however, two noteworthy cases in which not all the allolexes of a lexeme can have the same exposition. The first arises when two or more lexemes have in common a homographic allolex, but at least one of the lexemes has in addition an allolex not shared by the other lexeme(s). The homographic allolexes must have one exposition, different from that pertaining to the other allolex or allolexes. This shared exposition will contain rules for unraveling the homography—rules that would be otiose in the unshared expositions. An example of this situation is furnished by the Russian morphemes бред "delirium" and бред/бреж "to be delirious." Instead of one exposition for each morpheme, there will have to be one exposition for бред "delirium/to be delirious" and another for бреж "to be delirious."

The second case turns up when the identification of one or another allolex of a lexeme will serve to resolve the homography between two lexes which can occur contiguous to this lexeme. The different allolexes of this lexeme must then have separate expositions. A Russian example is the stem хозяин/хозяев "master, owner." Either allolex may occur with a suffixal lex -a, but the former allolex of this stem will show that the suffix represents the genitive singular morpheme, while the latter will show that it stands for nominative plural.

13. Organizing and Updating

The organization and coding of the dictionary for use by the program described here would be too tedious a job to be performed by hand, but it is relatively easy to construct a program which will enable the computer to do it. Such a program may be called the *dictionary adapter*. It will take as its input the dictionary in the form in which it is worked on by linguists, namely with the headings attached to the expositions and the entries arranged in alphabetical order of the headings.

The operations of the adapter fall into three stages. First it will separate the headings from the expositions and put the latter on tape to create the exposition list, at the same time forming the intermediate word for each exposition and associating this with its heading. In the second stage it will work with the headings to form the letter tables and truncate lists, thereby determining the intermediate address for each intermediate word. Finally, it will place the intermediate words at the locations indicated by their intermediate addresses to make the intermediate list.

5   Parsing

David G. Hays

1. Introduction

To parse a sentence is to relate it to a general description of a language. Languages are complex, and descriptions of them can be segmented into various components: phonological, syntactic, and semantic;[1] or phonemic, morphemic, lexemic, and sememic.[2] Parsing, in the widest sense, can likewise be segmented; the present discussion is confined to methods for syntactic, or lexemic, analysis of given sentences.

The input to a parser, commonly obtained by consultation of a dictionary, is therefore a string of sets of grammatical descriptions. Each set pertains to a unit occurrence; the units might be morphs, lexes, etc. The descriptions in any one set are alternative syntactic characterizations. If a set has two or more elements, the corresponding unit is syntactically ambiguous, and one objective of parsing is to eliminate ambiguities insofar as grammatical rules make some of the descriptions unacceptable in the context of the whole sentence.

Other objectives are recognition of linkages among units, of their grammatical roles, of full or partial parallels to other sentences, and of ellipsis or omission.[3] The output of the parser must serve as input to other programs, for semantic or sememic interpretation of the sentence; the general objective of parser design is to make the output appropriate to this use.

2. Grammatical Theory and Parser Design

Different theories of grammar require different kinds of parsers. The present discussion is chiefly about parsers for context-free phrase-structure, dependency, or mixed grammars.[4] In this case, a parser can consist of two main parts: a parsing logic (PL) routine, and a connectability test (CT) routine. The PL routine embodies the contiguity rule of the theory, whereas the CT routine determines the acceptability of certain combinations with respect to a given grammar.

A context-free phrase-structure grammar produces strings by rewriting individual symbols; rewriting b as xy in the string abc yields $axyc$, and re-

73

writing x as wz yields *awzyc*. The symbol x *covers wz*, and b covers *wzy*. The substring wz is a *constitute* of type x, with *constituents* w and z. To parse a string produced in this manner, it is necessary to find constitutes with constituents in the terminal string (e.g., wz, of type x); then constitutes of which the constituents are either terminal symbols or constitutes already discovered (e.g., xy, of type b); until a constitute is found that covers the whole string. Although a constitute can have more than two constituents, parsers assuming two in every case are adequate to illustrate all principles, and they are the only type discussed here.

Parsers for context-sensitive, transformational, and other kinds of grammars are essentially more complex. A brief description of some possible techniques follows the treatment of the context-free case.

3. Parsing in the Absence of Ambiguity

Assume a string of grammatical descriptions, say

$$g_1 g_2 \cdots g_n$$

Let p be a control variable denoting positions in the string; initially $p = 2$. The method of this PL routine is to parse the substring $g_1 g_2 \ldots g_p$, then add g_{p+1}.

For $p = 2$, the only question to be answered is whether $g_1 g_2$ is a constitute; the CT routine answers this question and supplies the type of the constitute, if any, say g_{12}. The PL routine then sets $p = 3$ and examines either $g_1 g_2 g_3$ or $g_{12} g_3$.

For $p = 3$, the first pair submitted to the CT routine is either $g_2 g_3$ or $g_{12} g_3$. If a new constitute covering the second and third units, with type g_{23}, is found, then the pair $g_1 g_{23}$ is tested. The possible results at this stage are displayed in Fig. 1.

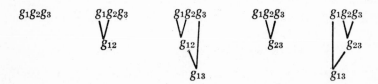

Fig. 1. Possible results of attempted phrase structure parsing.

For any p, the PL routine has to process a string of descriptions, whether of units in the terminal string or of constitutes formed earlier. It calls for a test of the rightmost pair; if the result is affirmative, it replaces the last two with a new one and again calls for a test, but if the result is negative it goes on to the next value of p.

This routine is inadequate if any unit is ambiguous, since it assumes one description per occurrence. Moreover, it assumes a special property in the grammar. Suppose xyz is to be parsed, and suppose also that xy is a constitute of type v, and yz one of type w. This PL routine would immediately replace xy with v and examine vz, but never test yz or xw.[5]

4. Backtracking

The PL routine of Sec. 3 can be put under the control of a backtracking program[6] in such a way as to allow for ambiguities. Assume a string of sets of grammatical descriptions, say

$$\{g_1{}^1, g_1{}^2, \ldots, g_1{}^{k_1}\} \ldots \{g_n{}^1, g_n{}^2, \ldots, g_n{}^{k_n}\}$$

Let $b_1, b_2, \ldots, b_n$ be backtrack control variables; initially $b_i = 1$ for each i. The PL routine operates just as before, except that it must choose one of the k_i distinct grammatical descriptions of the i-th unit. It chooses $g_i{}^{b_i}$, i.e., it consults the i-th backtrack control variable.

When the PL routine has gone through the whole string, its result is recorded if successful; then the program backtracks by finding the largest i such that $b_i < k_i$, adding 1 to b_i, setting $b_j = 1$ for all $j > i$, setting $p = i$, erasing all results involving the i-th or later units, and calling on the PL routine.

What this procedure does is to run systematically through all possible combinations of grammatical descriptions. If the last unit in the sentence has three descriptions, the backtrack procedure makes the PL routine attempt parsings using all three in turn. Then it moves to the next-to-last unit, changes the interpretation there, and goes through the three descriptions of the last unit once more.

To deal with the problem mentioned at the end of Sec. 3, more control variables must be introduced. Whenever the PL routine forms a constitute, it may thereby be preventing formation of another; hence, a control variable must be defined each time the CT routine gives an affirmative answer. Backtracking on these variables consists of disallowing constitutes in all possible combinations, so as to bring out all the rest.

The main value of backtracking is its ability to obtain *one* answer quickly; it can do so only if the ordering of descriptions puts the most commonly correct one first. The disadvantage is that partial analyses are discarded wholesale, only to be reconstructed in certain cases.

5. Simultaneous Partial Analysis

If all parsings are wanted, other techniques can avoid repetitious development of partial analyses. One method is to form and store all legitimate constitutes; the order of formation is crucial, but not uniquely determined.

The properties of a constitute are its type, or grammatical description; the identities of its constituents; the length of the terminal string it covers (i.e., how many unit occurrences); and the position of the covered string relative to the whole string (i.e., the ordinal of the first unit covered). These same properties, except for the identities of the constituents, also apply to the unit occurrences.

A parsing list is a sequence of (numbered) entries. Each entry has five parts: (1) a length L; (2) a position p; (3) a grammatical description g; (4) an entry number identifying a lefthand constituent; (5) an entry number identifying a righthand constituent. The entries with $L = 1$ refer to unit occurrences; the rest refer to constitutes. If a unit or constitute has two or more alternative grammatical descriptions, then two or more entries refer to it.

One PL routine that develops a parsing list moves through the sentence in the manner of the Sec. 3 routine. In this case, let p be the ordinal of the *last* unit covered by a constitute. Starting with control variable $p' = 1$, enter on the parsing list all the grammatical descriptions of the first unit (see Fig. 2). Advancing to $p' = 2$, set control variable $L' = 1$ and enter

Entry Number	L	p	g	LHC	RHC
(1)	1	1	g_1^1		
(2)	1	1	g_1^2		
(3)	1	2	g_2^1		
(4)	1	2	g_2^2		
(5)	2	2	g_{12}^1	1	4
(6)	2	2	g_{12}^2	2	3
(7)	1	3	g_3^1		
(8)	2	3	g_{23}^1	3	7
(9)	3	3	g_{13}^1	5	7
(10)	3	3	g_{13}^2	1	8
(11)	1	4	g_4^1		
(12)	2	4	g_{34}^1	7	11
(13)	3	4	g_{24}^1	8	11
(14)	3	4	g_{24}^2	4	12
(15)	4	4	g_{14}^1	9	11
(16)	4	4	g_{14}^2	6	12
(17)	4	4	g_{14}^3	2	13

Fig. 2. Example of a parsing list, where L = length, p = position, g = grammatical description (g_{jk}^i is the i-th distinct description of a constitute covering positions j through k), LHC = lefthand constituent, RHC = righthand constituent (denoted by entry number).

the descriptions of the second unit. Next, advance to $L' = 2$, and form all possible constitutes. The constitutents must both have $L = 1$, and must have $p = 1$ and $p = 2$ respectively; the PL routine runs through all pairings of grammatical descriptions (in Fig. 2, entries 1 and 2 are paired with 3 and 4: 1–3, 1–4, 2–3, and 2–4), submitting each pair to a CT routine and entering each affirmative result on the parsing list. Since L' is limited to values no larger than p', this ends the cycle with $p' = 2$.

Advancing to $p' = 3$, and resetting to $L' = 1$, the routine enters the descriptions of the third unit on the parsing list. With $L' = 2$, it checks for constitutes covering the second and third units. Then, with $L' = 3$, it must perform two kinds of pairings: (1) Each entry with $L = 1$, $p = 3$ is paired with each entry with $L = 2$ and $p = 2$. (2) Each entry with $L = 2$, $p = 3$ is paired with each entry with $L = 1$, $p = 1$.

Parsing of a sentence of n units continues until $p' = n$. In general, the procedure takes consecutive values of p'. For each value of p', it takes all values of L' from 1 to p'. For fixed p' and L', it pairs all entries with $L = k$, $p = p'$ against all entries with $L = L' - k$, $p = p' - k$; here k, the control variable for the length of the lefthand constituent, takes all values from 1 to $L' - 1$.

This PL routine has five control variables: p', L', k, and two more to count through alternative grammatical descriptions of left and right constituents. Interchanging the order of p' and L' yields the original routine due to John Cocke. In this version, L' runs from 1 to n. For each value of L', p' (interpreted as ordinal of the first unit covered) runs from 1 to $n - L' + 1$, so that all constitutes of length L' are formed at a certain stage. For fixed L' and p', the third control variable k runs from 1 to $L' - 1$; the left constituent has $p = p'$, $L = k$, and the right has $p = p' + k$, $L = L' - k$.

Either version has the advantage of applying the CT routine to any pair of constituents only once. The disadvantage of greatest practical importance is the large number of entries put on the parsing list—and not used— when the CT routine is as imprecise, and the language as ambiguous, as in current work with English. Each constitute is accepted or rejected in accordance with internal criteria, but can be used later only if a partner can be found for it elsewhere in the sentence. Avoiding excessive storage requirements is therefore an important design problem.7

6. Some Ancillary Devices

A few techniques for improving the performance of PL routines have been published.

With some grammars, it is possible to form two constitutes that cover the same part of a sentence and have the same grammatical description;

they differ only with respect to internal structure. For example, the grammar might allow x to be rewritten as either av or wc; then if v can be written as bc and w as ab, the string abc is covered by x in two ways. In a parsing list, there would be two entries (see Fig. $3(a)$); each could be a constituent of any larger constitute accepting either. By reducing these two entries to one, the number of entries placed on the list thereafter can be reduced. One technique is shown in Fig. $3(b)$; instead of showing the identity of the constituents, the parsing list shows where a list of pairs can be found. This device is due to Cocke.

Although the entries on the parsing list must be kept accessible as long as any constitute might be formed from them, they need not be kept indefinitely. If the sentence to be parsed has n units, then (with n odd) the unit at position $p = (n+1)/2$ can never be used after constitutes of length $L = (n+1)/2$ have been formed. Likewise, constitutes of any length located near the center of the string become unusable as soon as constitutes long enough to cover them and everything on either side have been formed. This device, due to Robert Dupchak, entails complicated reassignment of storage and, hence, would be attractive only in applications where lack of storage caused grave difficulties.

If operation is to be fast, location of entries with given values of p and L must be quick. When the main control variable is p', all entries with fixed p are consecutive on the list, and L is nondecreasing for fixed p. A directory can be constructed, showing for each value of p the number

Entry Number	L	p	g	LHC	RHC
(1)	1	1	a		
(2)	1	2	b		
(3)	2	2	w	1	2
(4)	1	3	c		
(5)	2	3	v	2	4
(6)	3	3	x	3	4
(7)	3	3	x	1	5

Fig. 3(a). Parsing list with duplicate entries.

Entry Number	L	p	g	LHC	RHC	Auxiliary List Entry Number	LHC	RHC
—	—	—	—	—	—	(*1–1)	3	4
(6)	3	3	x	*1		(*1–2)	1	5

Fig. 3(b). Elimination of duplicates by use of auxiliary.

of the first entry on the parsing list for which that value obtains. Consider the first routine of Sec. 5, and note how it operates on the list of Fig. 2. When $p' = 4$, $L' = 4$, $k = 1$, entry 14 has just been constructed. The righthand constituent to be tested is entry 11; it is to be paired with entries 9 and 10. Next, with $k = 2$, entry 12 is to be paired with entries 5 and 6. Finally, with $k = 3$, entries 13 and 14 are to be paired with entries 1 and 2. The righthand constituents are always taken in order, for fixed p' and L', as k runs through its range (but for fixed k a subcycle may be required). The lefthand constituents wanted need not be first or last among those with common p; the directory is helpful, but searches are still needed —as when the directory points to entry 3, the first with $p = 2$, and entry 5 must be sought. Of course, if space is available, the directory can point to the beginning of each $p\text{-}L$ group.

7. Dependency Parsing

Instead of treating the constituencies of sentences, a dependency grammar treats the direct interconnections of smallest units.[8] The difference is apparent from comparison of Fig. 1 with Fig. 4; the auxiliary symbols for phrases (e.g., g_{12}, g_{13}) do not appear in Fig. 4, but the distinction between

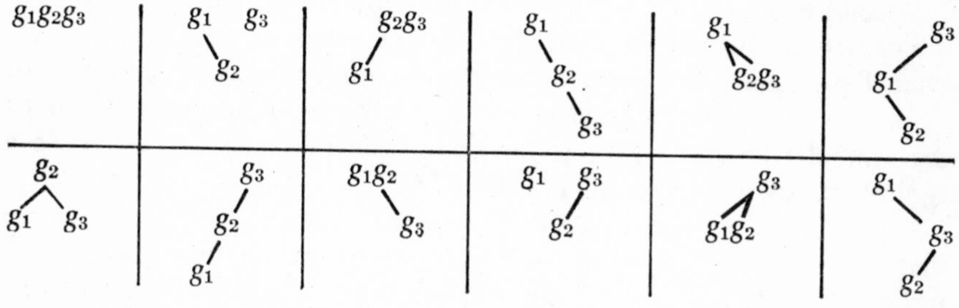

Fig. 4. Possible results of attempted dependency parsing.

dependent (lower) and governor (upper) makes for more distinct diagrams.

Nevertheless, a phrase-structure parser can be converted into a dependency parser with only a minor alteration. The parsing list must carry one additional kind of information: whether the governor is in the lefthand or righthand constituent. An algorithm for constructing dependency diagrams is then straightforward. Begin with an entry of the form

$$(i)\ n\,p\,g\,j\,k\,t$$

where n is the length of the parsed sentence, and t marks one of the constituents, described in entry j or k, as governor. Assume it marks j; the other case is symmetric. Start a list of governors with j and sublist of dependents of j:

$$j : k$$

Now consult entry j; if it has constituents, replace j with the entry number of the governing constituent, say j', and list the dependent constituent, say k', after k:

$$j' : k, k'$$

Otherwise, entry j describes a unit occurrence; replace j with its position number and tag it:

$$pos(j) : k$$

Repeat this step until a unit occurrence is reached; its sublist contains one entry number for each of its dependents. Proceed in the same manner with the dependents (e.g., k), forming for each a sublist of its dependents; but now whenever one entry number replaces another, it does so in two places, once as governor and once as the dependent. The result is a list of position numbers of governors, each accompanied by a sublist of its dependents' position numbers.

8. Context-Sensitive Parsing

A context-free grammar allows a symbol to be rewritten in any context; a context-sensitive grammar specifies the contexts in which rewriting of a symbol is allowed. The difficulty that this sensitivity poses is merely that the contextual symbol can cover a longer substring than that covered by the symbol whose rewriting is restricted. The usefulness of length as a control variable is therefore impaired.

For example, suppose that x can be written, following w, as yz; suppose that y and z cover substrings each of length two, so that x should be recognized when $L' = 4$. If w covers a substring of length five or more, its existence is unknown at that stage. Moreover, if position is the main control variable, contextual requirements following the restricted symbol are unmanageable.

One technique for circumventing this difficulty, due to Cocke, is to parse any given sentence as if the grammar were context free. The result of parsing is a statement purporting to describe the production of the sentence by the grammar. An attempt to carry out the described production, but with attention to context, fails if the contextual symbols are absent altogether. A parsing result is discarded if the production it describes fails.9

9. Transformational Parsers

A transformational grammar produces sentences by developing strings and associated structural descriptions, using rewrite rules, then operating on the results. The applicability of an operation can be conditioned by features of structure—i.e., the history of rewritings—as well as by context within the latest string. Operations can alter structures as well as strings. It is known that transformational grammars can produce sets of strings and also sets of structures that simpler grammars cannot.

The difficulty of parsing sentences produced transformationally is great. One method suggested early was analysis by synthesis; the idea was to produce sentences until the one to be parsed was observed. Various techniques intended to guarantee production of sentences rather like the given sentence were proposed, but the amount of computation that would be required is still high.[10]

Another approach[11] is to construct a context-free phrase-structure grammar that produces all of the sentences produced by a given transformational grammar (in general, other sentences will be produced as well) and assigns to each of them all the structures assigned by the transformational grammar (and, in general, excess structures). Parsing with the simpler grammar does not decide whether a string is a sentence, or what structure it has; *surface* parsing does no more than yield a set of hypotheses.

The next phase in this approach is to invert each transformation. Each transformation is applicable to a certain range R of structural descriptions, and works certain alterations on them; it maps R onto a set R' of new structures. The class R' must be described, and a rule must be formulated that maps any member of R' back onto the member (or members) of R from which the transformation would produce it. If it is necessary or convenient to do so, a class including R' may be described; later phases eliminate erroneous analyses.

It is at this stage that a PL routine peculiar to transformational theory would be expected. In fact, the general theory of transformations permits a very wide range of rule types; it allows different kinds of classes of underlying structures (produced by rewrite rules alone); and it permits organization of the transformation rules in diverse ways. A PL routine for the full transformational theory would be excessively complex, but fortunately most authors believe that less than the full theory is required in the description of natural languages. They are not yet fully in accord, however, with respect to the kinds of simplifications or restrictions that would be most suitable. Hence, various parsing logics are needed, each determining in its own way what transformations are applicable to the objects it works on. In general, it must be noted that applicability of an inverse transformation at a certain moment during parsing does not guarantee that the object to which it can be applied can be obtained only by means of it. Thus allowance must be made for local ambiguity.

After an object ostensibly produced by rewrite rules alone is obtained by the parser, it must be parsed in its turn by the rewrite-rule grammar—unless, of course, its parsing is explicit in the form first obtained.

Finally, verification procedures are applied. These procedures check whether the rewrite rules could produce the underlying object; and whether the transformational component could produce from that object the string submitted for parsing. Erroneous hypotheses are eliminated here, and parsing is complete.

10. Acknowledgments

Over the years, I have profited from discussions of parsing with many specialists. Among them I must mention in particular John Cocke, Martin Kay (who is currently engaged in a broad study of parsing methods), A. F. Parker-Rhodes, Sheila Greibach, and Sydney M. Lamb. Some of the ideas in this paper were discussed briefly and informally at the 1962 Congress of the International Federation for Information Processing.

References

1. Jerrold J. Katz and Paul M. Postal, *An Integrated Theory of Linguistic Descriptions*, Research Monograph No. 26, Massachusetts Institute of Technology Press, Cambridge, Massachusetts (1964).

2. Sydney M. Lamb, "Epilegomena to a Theory of Language," *Romance Philology*, in press.

3. A fairly broad treatment of objectives is given by Noam Chomsky, *Aspects of the Theory of Syntax*, Massachusetts Institute of Technology Press, Cambridge, Massachusetts (1965).

4. See, for example, Noam Chomsky, "Formal Properties of Grammars," in R. Duncan Luce, Robert R. Bush and Eugene Galanter, eds., *Handbook of Mathematical Psychology*, John Wiley & Sons, New York, Vol. II (1963), pp. 323–418.

5. The PL routine of this section resembles, but is oversimplified in comparison with, that of A. F. Parker-Rhodes, R. McKinnon Wood, M. Kay, and P. Bratley, *The Cambridge Language Research Unit Computer Program for Syntactic Analysis*, M. L. 136, Cambridge Language Research Unit, Cambridge, England.

6 Solomon W. Golomb and Leonard D. Baumert, "Backtrack Programming," *Journal of the Association for Computing Machinery*, vol. 12, no. 4 (October 1965), pp. 516-524.

7. For an extensive application of Cocke's routine, see Jane Robinson and Shirley Marks, *Parse: A System for Automatic Syntactic Analysis of English Text*, Memorandum RM-4654-PR, The RAND Corporation, Santa Monica, California (September 1965).

8. David G. Hays, "Dependency Theory: A Formalism and some Observations," *Language*, Vol. 40, No. 4 (October-December 1964), pp. 511–525.

9. Context-sensitive parsers are discussed by T. V. Griffiths, "Turing Machine Recognizers for General Rewriting Systems," in *IEEE Symposium on Switching Circuit Theory and Logical Design* (1964), pp. 47–56.

10. G. H. Matthews, "Analysis by Synthesis of Sentences of Natural Languages," in *1961 International Conference on Machine Translation of Languages and Applied Language Analysis*, Her Majesty's Stationery Office, London (1962), pp. 531–542.

11. Arnold M. Zwicky, Joyce Friedman, Barbara C. Hall, and Donald E. Walker, "The MITRE Syntactic Analysis Procedure for Transformational Grammars," *Proceedings of the 1965 Fall Joint Computer Conference*, Spartan Books, Washington, D.C. (1965), pp. 317-326.

6 The Predictive Analyzer and a Path Elimination Technique

Susumu Kuno

1. The Predictive Analyzer

A predictive analyzer produces for a given sentence all possible syntactic interpretations compatible with the current version of the predictive grammar. The predictive grammar G' comprises rules of the form:

$$(Z, c) \mid Y_1 \ldots Y_m \qquad (m \geqslant 1)$$
$$(Z, c) \mid \Lambda \qquad (m = 0)$$

where Z, Y_i, are intermediate symbols (i.e., syntactic structures), c is a terminal symbol (i.e., syntactic word class) and Λ denotes the absence of any symbol. (Z, c) is called an argument pair. (SE, prn) | VP PD, for example, indicates that a sentence (SE) can be initiated by a prn (personal pronoun in the nominative case) if the prn is followed by a predicate (VP) and a period (PD). A fragment of our current English grammar is shown in Kuno and Oettinger [1, 2]. It has been proved by Greibach [3, 4, 5] that G' is an exact inverse* of a standard-form grammar G whose rules are of the form

$$Z \to c Y_1 \ldots Y_m$$

where $(Z, c) \mid Y_1 \ldots Y_m$ is a rule in G', or

$$Z \to c$$

where $(Z, c) \mid \Lambda$ is a rule in G'.

Since Greibach has proved that every context-free language can be gen-

---

Note: This work was performed in the Computation Laboratory of Harvard University, supported in part by the National Science Foundation under grants GN-162 and GN-329. Reprinted with the permission of author and publisher from *Communications of the Association for Computing Machinery*, Vol. 8, No. 7 (July 1965), pp. 453–462.

* If an analyzer with grammar A accepts all and only those sentences that are generated by B, we call A an exact inverse of B.

erated by a standard-form grammar, the Harvard analyzer could accept any context-free language given a suitable predictive grammar.*

Consider a predictive grammar which does not contain more than one rule with the same argument pair, and an input string of words each of which is associated with a unique terminal symbol. The analysis of the sequence of terminal symbols $c_1 \ldots c_n$ is initiated with a pushdown store (PDS) containing some designated initial symbol. At word k in the course of the analysis of the string, an argument pair (Z, c_k) is formed from the intermediate symbol Z topmost in the PDS and the current terminal symbol c_k. If a rule with this argument pair is not found in the grammar, the input string is ill-formed (ungrammatical). If it is found, we say that Z has been fulfilled by the rule $(Z, c_k) \mid Y_1 \ldots Y_m$ (or $\mid \Lambda$), or simply by c_k. A set of new intermediate symbols $Y_1 \ldots Y_m$ or Λ then replaces the topmost intermediate symbol Z of the pushdown store and the analysis flow goes to $k + 1$. The input string is well formed (grammatical) if the last terminal symbol c_n is processed yielding an empty PDS. A set of standard-form rules corresponding to the predictive rules used for the analysis of the string gives the derivational history of the string in the original standard-form grammar.

Actually, a grammar may have more than one rule with the same argument pair. Also, a word in an input string may be associated with more than one terminal symbol. Therefore, a mechanism for cycling through all possible combinations of these rules and terminal symbols must be superimposed on the simple pushdown store machine described in the previous paragraph.

Let $W(k)$ be a set of terminal symbols corresponding to word k in a given sentence and $S(k)$ a set of rules in the grammar whose argument pairs contain a member of $W(k)$. $S(k)$, then, defines a subset of the grammar which will be used for the processing of the kth word of this particular sentence. There are various techniques for referencing all the members of $S(k)$, but for the description of the cycling mechanism of the predictive analyzer, let it suffice to say that the first member of $S(k)$ is located at address $I(k)$ and its last member at $L(k)$.

The program utilizes two sets of registers: $A(i)$ and $B(i)$ for $i = 1, 2, \ldots, n$. Prior to the initiation of the analysis of the sentence, $A(i)$, the $S(i)$ boundary register, is set to $[I(i), L(i)]$. The active rule pointer $B(i)$ is set to $I(i)$ for all the values of i (see Table 1). Let $Z(k)$ be the topmost symbol in the PDS prior to the processing of a rule at k, and let $sr(B(k))$

---

* Given a context-free grammar G'', we can automatically construct a standard-form grammar G' which generates the same language as G'' does. However, the structural descriptions assigned to a given sentence by G' are usually different from the ones assigned to the same sentence by G''. See Sec. 2(5) for further discussions on structural descriptions.

Table 1. Registers Used for Cycling Through Rules

i		1	...	k	...	n
$S(i)$ Boundary Register	$A(i)$	$[I(1), L(1)]$		$[I(k), L(k)]$		$[I(n), L(n)]$
Active Rule Pointer	$B(i)$	$I(1)$		$I(k)$		$I(n)$

Table 2. Basic Flow of a Predictive Analyzer

Step 0. Store the initial symbol X in the PDS.
Set $k = 1$.

Step 1. Does the argument pair of $sr(B(k))$ contain $Z(k)$? (Note: $Z(1) = X$.)
If no, go to step 6.

Step 2. Replace $Z(k)$ in the PDS by $sr(B(k))$'s set of new intermediate symbols $Y_1 .... Y_m$ (possibly Λ).

Step 3. $k + 1 \rightarrow k$
$k > n$? If no, go to step 1.

Step 4. Is the PDS empty? If no, go to step 7.

Step 5. Output $sr(B(i))$ for $i = 1, 2, \ldots, n$. Go to step 7.

Step 6. $B(k) + q \rightarrow B(k)$.
Note: q is a constant to be added to $B(k)$ to obtain the next rule in $S(k)$.
$B(k) > L(k)$? If yes, $I(k) \rightarrow B(k)$, and go to step 7.
If no, go to step 1.

Step 7. $k - 1 \rightarrow k$.
$k = 0$? If yes, the sentence has been exhaustively processed. Exit.
If no, reconstruct the PDS configuration of k, and go to step 6.

be the rule currently to be used at k. The flow of the analysis procedure is shown in Table 2 (the explanation of "reconstruct the PDS configuration of k" in step 7 is given in the next paragraph).

Assume that, at k in the course of the analysis of a sentence, the PDS contains two intermediate symbols $\overline{P \mid R}$, and that, due to the rule $(P, a) \mid C_1 \cdots C_m$, we have the new PDS configuration $\overline{C_1 \mid \cdots \mid C_m \mid R}$ at $k + 1$. In step 7 of the analysis flow, the analysis path has to go back from $k + 1$ to k, and the PDS configuration $\overline{P \mid R}$ has to be recontructed out of the current configuration $\overline{C_1 \mid \cdots \mid C_m \mid R}$. In order to make this process efficient, the program uses two additional sets of registers $\alpha(i)$ and $\beta(i)$. $\alpha(i)$ is used to store $Z(i)$, and $\beta(i)$ is used to store the position of $Z(i)$ in the PDS counting from the bottom. Therefore, in the example under discussion the four registers at k and $k + 1$ contain the information shown in Table 3. Now, given $\overline{C_1 \mid \cdot \cdot \cdot \mid C_m \mid R}$ at $k+1$, the PDS configuration at k can be restored by erasing $\beta(k)$-th, $(\beta(k)+1)$-st, $\cdot\cdot\cdot$, $(\beta(k+1))$-st symbols in the current PDS and then by storing $\alpha(k)$ in the $\beta(k)$-th position in the PDS.

Table 3. Registers for the Reconstruction of PDS Configuration

i	k	$k+1$
$A(i)$	$[I(k), L(k)]$	$[I(k+1), L(k+1)]$
$B(i)$	XXX	XXX
$\alpha(i)$	P	C_1
$\beta(i)$	2	$2+m-1$

2. Characteristic Features of a Predictive Analyzer

As has been shown in the previous section, given a PDS configuration at word k, the number of analysis branches which emanate from k and reach $k+1$ is equal to $f(S(k+1))$, the number (possibly zero) of rules in $S(k+1)$ which have the same intermediate symbol in the argument pair as the PDS's topmost symbol $Z(k)$. From each of the PDS configurations thus formed at $k+1$, $f(S(k+2))$ (possibly zero) analysis branches emanate. With the use of the current English grammar, the number of analysis branches grows exponentially with sentence length for natural English sentences. In order to reduce this exponential effect to a linear one, a new repetitive path elimination technique has been devised and incorporated in the basic flow of the predictive analysis procedure described in Table 2. Before going into the details of this technique, it is worthwhile to compare a predictive analyzer with the immediate constituent (IC) analyzer of The RAND Corporation* to clarify some salient differences between the two systems.

It is shown below that a predictive analyzer, in its basic flow, achieves efficiency in core storage requirement at the sacrifice of efficiency in processing time, while an IC analyzer† achieves efficiency in the latter at a sacrifice of efficiency in the former. It is shown in Section 3 that the tech-

---

* The predictive analyzer at Harvard and the IC analyzer at The RAND Corporation are the only currently operational systems with considerably detailed English grammars. Models of context-free grammars are also used in connection with programming languages. See Floyd 6 for procedures of syntactic analysis developed for translation of programming languages.

† Throughout this paper, the term "an IC analyzer" is used specifically to refer to a context-free recognition procedure based on the same principle as the RAND analyzer is.

nique for repetitive path elimination that has been devised for a predictive analyzer is a means for making the predictive analyzer efficient both in core storage requirement and processing time.

The IC analyzer of The RAND Corporation is based on Cocke's [7] parsing algorithm* and utilizes Robinson's [9] IC grammar for English. The grammar is an exact inverse of a binary grammar: $(A, B) \mid Z$ is a rule in an IC grammar where $Z \to A B$ is a rule in the corresponding binary grammar, where Z is an intermediate symbol and A and B are either intermediate or terminal.

The parsing algorithm of an IC analyzer works as follows: initially, all two-word combinations are tested to see if they form syntactic constitutes.† If yes, the intermediate symbols representing the constitutes are stored in core together with the identification of the position of their constituents. Next, all three-word combinations are tested. The string $k, k + 1, k + 2$, for example, consists of immediate constituents $((k, k + 1), k + 2)$ or $(k, (k + 1, k + 2))$, and so on. If $(k, k + 1)$ has not been identified previously as a constitute, $((k, k + 1), k + 2)$ is rejected immediately. If it has, the intermediate symbol representing $(k, k + 1)$ and the one representing $k + 2$ are looked up in the grammar to see if they form a constitute. If they do, the intermediate symbol representing the whole constitute is stored in core with the identification of its two constituents $(k, k + 1)$ and $k + 2$. The same analysis procedure applies to $(k, (k + 1, k + 2))$, and so forth.

For the processing of the four-word combination $k, k + 1, k + 2, k + 3$, the possible bracketings are $(k, (k + 1, k + 2, k + 3))$, $((k, k + 1), (k + 2, k + 3))$, and $((k, k + 1, k + 2), k + 3)$. It is to be noted that if two-word combinations $(k, k + 1)$ and $(k + 2, k + 3)$, and three-word combinations $(k + 1, k + 2, k + 3)$ and $(k, k + 1, k + 2)$, contained in this four-word combination are syntactic constitutes, they must have been previously identified as such and must have been recorded in core with their identified intermediate symbols. The analysis proceeds to larger and larger constitutes until the n-word combination (n is the number of words in the sentence) has been processed. If there is an intermediate symbol of *"sentence"* identified for this n-word combination, the history of the path which has led to this designated symbol corresponds to an immediate constituent analysis of the sentence.

Now we are ready to compare some of the characteristic features of a predictive analyzer and an IC analyzer.

---

* Sakai [8] has independently developed an IC analysis algorithm very similar to Cocke's.

† Two substrings α and β, corresponding to A and B, respectively, of $(A, B) \mid Z$ are called (*immediate*) *constituents*, and the entire string $\alpha\beta$ corresponding to Z is called a *constitute*.

(1) A predictive analyzer, due to the cycling mechanism described in the previous section, keeps track of possible analysis paths utilizing a single PDS at any one time. Given the maximum value of n allowable for a given system (max $n = 72$ for the current system on an IBM 7094), there is no problem of core storage overflow. An IC analyzer, on the other hand, stores all the intermediate constitutes in core for easy access in the processing of larger constitutes. This produces a problem of core storage overflow, and sometimes the current RAND analyzer, with the current Robinson grammar, actually causes overflow for sentences with 30 words. This is considered by the author to be the major drawback of an IC analyzer as compared with a predictive analyzer.

(1a) An IC analyzer recognizes, and can list as by-products, all the well-formed substrings contained in the sentence, while a predictive analyzer, in its basic flow of logic, does not recognize well-formed substrings.

(2) In an IC analyzer, once a given combination of words is identified as a syntactic constitute with a certain set of intermediate symbols assigned to it, the same combination will be regarded as a unit for the processing of larger constitutes; that is, no internal analysis of the constitute will be repeated. In a predictive analyzer, on the other hand, whenever an intermediate symbol becomes topmost in the PDS more than once at a given word position k, all rules in $S(k)$ are processed repeatedly.

For example, assume that the input sentence "TIME FLIES LIKE AN ARROW AND THEY ARE FLYING PLANES." is to be analyzed by a predictive analyzer. The two clauses in the sentence are triply ambiguous and their ambiguities are mutually independent.

TIME FLIES LIKE AN ARROW

1. Time passes as quickly as an arrow.
2. A species of flies called "time flies" are fond of an arrow.
3. You shall time the flies which are like an arrow. (*Or* You shall, as quickly as an arrow, time the flies.)

THEY ARE FLYING PLANES

a. They are planes which are flying.
b. The facts are that the flying planes (over the hill). (*Cf.* The facts are that the flying kills.)
c. These people are flying the planes.

After the first interpretation of the first clause is obtained and the co-ordinating conjunction is processed, the PDS contains SE as the topmost intermediate symbol (see Table 4). Three interpretations a, b and c are obtained for the second clause. The analysis path eventually backs up to the beginning of the sentence, and the second interpretation for the first

Table 4. Repetitive Analysis Paths
Time Flies Like an Arrow and They are Flying Planes

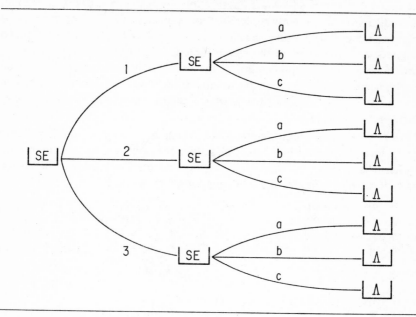

clause is obtained. SE becomes topmost in the PDS again after the processing of "AND". Now, all the analysis branches that were traversed before when SE became topmost for the first time have to be traversed again. The three interpretations of "THEY ARE FLYING PLANES" are rediscovered one by one. The same situation arises when the third interpretation of "TIME FLIES LIKE AN ARROW" is obtained and when SE becomes topmost in the PDS for the third time at the same word position.

Since the number of active paths at a given word position can easily reach the order of 10,000, and since there are approximately 80 distinct intermediate symbols currently recognized, a given rule at a given word position may very easily be processed hundreds of times in the current English analyzer. This is considered by the author to be the major drawback of a predictive analyzer as opposed to an IC analyzer.

(3) A predictive analyzer produces multiple analyses of a given sentence one by one whenever the end of the sentence is reached with an empty PDS. An IC analyzer, on the other hand, produces multiple analyses of the sentence simultaneously when the n-word combination has been processed with one or more resulting intermediate symbols. In cases when it is desirable to terminate the analysis procedure of a given sentence (a) after

the first analysis has been obtained, (b) after a limited processing time is exceeded, or (c) after an analysis has been obtained which is regarded as desirable by man-machine communication or by some arbitrary criterion, a predictive analyzer is quite flexible and can meet any one of these three requirements. An IC analyzer, on the other hand, produces either no analysis or all analyses of the whole sentence. If the maximum processing time is exceeded and processing of the sentence has to be terminated, no analysis of the sentence can be obtained. However, as was mentioned in (1a), the well-formed substrings of the length that has been reached so far can be obtained.

(4) A standard-form grammar, of which a predictive grammar is an exact inverse, usually has more rules than the context-free grammar from which it is derived and to which it is equivalent. Consider a context-free grammar which contains the following set of ten rules:*

1.	SE $\rightarrow$ NP VP PD	(cf. *"This is true."*)
2.	SE $\rightarrow$ NP PA SE	(cf. *"It being Sunday, we have no school."*)
3.	SG $\rightarrow$ NP VP	(cf. "I think that *it is true.*")
4.	SG' $\rightarrow$ NP VP'	(cf. "This is what *I like.*")
5.	NP $\rightarrow$ T N	(cf. *"the boy"*)
6.	NP $\rightarrow$ A N	(cf. *"good boys"*)
7.	NP $\rightarrow$ prn	(cf. *"they"*)
8.	NP $\rightarrow$ nou	(cf. *"boys"*)
9.	T $\rightarrow$ art	
10.	A $\rightarrow$ adj†	

An equivalent standard-form grammar can be constructed by replacing the leftmost symbol Y_1 of the right-hand expression of a rule, if it is intermediate, by the right-hand expression of each of the Y_1-rules. The process is repeated until the leftmost symbol of the right-hand expression of all the rules becomes terminal. For example, the intermediate symbol NP is the leftmost symbol in the right-hand expression of rule 1. Therefore, NP is replaced by the right-hand expression of NP-rules 5, 6, 7 and 8.

$$1\text{-}5. \quad SE \rightarrow NP\ VP\ PD \rightarrow T\ N\ VP\ PD$$
$$1\text{-}6. \quad SE \rightarrow NP\ VP\ PD \rightarrow A\ N\ VP\ PD$$
$$1\text{-}7. \quad SE \rightarrow NP\ VP\ PD \rightarrow prn\ VP\ PD$$
$$1\text{-}8. \quad SE \rightarrow NP\ VP\ PD \rightarrow nou\ VP\ PD$$

Since T and A of rules 1-5 and 1-6 are still intermediate symbols, they are replaced by the right-hand expressions of rules 9 and 10, respectively.

---

* Terminal symbols are represented by small letters and intermediate symbols by capital letters.

† SE: sentence, NP: noun phrase, VP: predicate, VP': predicate with a missing object, PD: period, PA: participial phrase, SG: declarative clause, SG': declarative clause with a missing object, T: article, A: adjective, N: noun.

1-5-9.   SE → NP VP PD → T N VP PD → art N VP PD
1-6-10. SE → NP VP PD → A N VP PD → adj N VP PD

The standard-form grammar equivalent to the one mentioned above contains the following 20 rules:

$1', 2', 3', 4'.$

$$SE \rightarrow \left\{ \begin{array}{l} art\ N \\ adj\ N \\ prn \\ nou \end{array} \right\} VP\ PD$$

$5', 6',' 7', 8'.$

$$SE \rightarrow \left\{ \begin{array}{l} art\ N \\ adj\ N \\ prn \\ nou \end{array} \right\} PA\ SE$$

$9', 10', 11', 12'.$

$$SG \rightarrow \left\{ \begin{array}{l} art\ N \\ adj\ N \\ prn \\ nou \end{array} \right\} VP$$

$13', 14', 15', 16'.$

$$SG' \rightarrow \left\{ \begin{array}{l} art\ N \\ adj\ N \\ prn \\ nou \end{array} \right\} VP'$$

$17', 18'.$

$$NP \rightarrow \left\{ \begin{array}{l} art \\ adj \end{array} \right\} N$$

$19'.$ $NP \rightarrow prn$
$20'.$ $NP \rightarrow nou$

If a rule of a context-free grammar has a terminal symbol c in the right-hand expression, but not as its leftmost symbol, c is replaced by a new intermediate symbol C, and a new rule $C \rightarrow c$ is added to the standard-form grammar.

The algorithm described above cannot be successfully applied when the original context-free grammar contains a rule or a set of rules which allows unbounded left-branchings. For example, if the grammar with rules 1 through 10 also contained

11.   NP   → NP AND NP
12.   AND → and

an infinite number of standard-form rules would be generated by the conversion algorithm:

NP → art N
NP → art N AND NP
NP → art N AND NP . . . AND NP

Greibach [3, 5] has shown that there is a method for converting unbounded left-branching structures to unbounded right-branching structures, preserving the same degree of ambiguity. In the example under discussion, the loop AND NP will be given a new name, say ANN. Rules 5, 6 and 11 of the original context-free grammar will be replaced by the following set of standard-form rules:

$$NP \rightarrow \left\{ \begin{array}{c} art \\ adj \end{array} \right\} N$$

$$NP \rightarrow \left\{ \begin{array}{c} art \\ adj \end{array} \right\} N \; ANN$$

$$ANN \rightarrow and \; NP$$

$$ANN \rightarrow and \; NP \; ANN$$

In an IC grammar, a set of NP-rules appears only once, while in a predictive grammar, it appears as many times as the number of constitutes whose first constituent is an NP (SE, SE, SG, SG′, and NP in the example under discussion). Therefore, with regard to the size of grammars, a predictive grammar is usually less simple and less economical than an equivalent IC grammar.

(5) A standard-form grammar does not impose any theoretical limitation on the number of intermediate symbols in the right-hand expressions of its rules:

$$Z \rightarrow cY_1 \ldots Y_m \qquad\qquad (m \geqslant 1)$$
$$Z \rightarrow c$$

This feature provides the predictive analyzer with some advantage over an IC grammar. It is not always easy to write a grammar for a natural language with only binary branching rules. For example, the context-free rewrite rule:

$$SE \rightarrow MORE \; NP' \; VP \; THAN\text{-}CLAUSE$$

for sentences such as "More people came than expected." will have to be replaced by a set of binary rules such as:

$$SE \rightarrow NP_{more} \; VP_{than}$$
$$NP_{more} \rightarrow MORE \; NP'$$
$$VP_{than} \rightarrow VP \; THAN\text{-}CLAUSE$$

while it can be represented by a single rule in a predictive grammar:

$$(SE, more) \mid NP' \; VP \; THAN\text{-}CLAUSE$$

In general, both a standard-form grammar and an IC grammar require more rules than an arbitrary context-free grammar to which they are equivalent. However, it is important to notice the difference in the nature of the expansion in size of two types of grammars. In the case of a standard-form grammar, as has been explained in (4), the expansion is due to replacing Y_1 of $Z \rightarrow Y_1 \cdots Y_m$ by Y_1-rules. Where the original context-free grammar contained p Y_1-rules and q rules whose leftmost symbol of the right-hand expression is Y_1, an equivalent standard-form grammar contains at least $p \times q$ rules. In the case of an IC analyzer, as mentioned in (5), if the original context-free grammar contained a rule with more than two symbols in the right-hand expression, only this rule is replaced by a set of new binary rules, and the expansion does not extend over other rules in the grammar. While a standard-form grammar has redundancy whenever $q > 1$, an IC grammar does not have any redundant information in it. For grammars of natural languages, the expansion of the size of grammar due to (4) seems to be a more serious problem than that due to (5).

It should also be noticed that the structural descriptions assigned to a given sentence by an arbitrary context-free grammar are not usually equivalent to those assigned to the same sentence by either an equivalent standard-form grammar or an equivalent IC grammar. Therefore, when a predictive analyzer or an IC analyzer is used not only as an acceptance device for sentences of a context-free language, but as a device for assigning structural descriptions to accepted sentences, we need a mechanism for mapping the distorted structural descriptions of either analyzer into the correct structural descriptions which would have been assigned by the original context-free grammar.

(6) Partly to make up for the drawback of repetitive path processing, efficiency techniques such as (a) a simple shaper test (due to W. Bossert and D. Isenberg) and (b) a generalized shaper test (due to W. Plath) have been developed for the predictive analyzer.* In these two techniques, a rule applicable at a given word position on a path is rejected for this particular path if its new set of intermediate symbols produces a PDS configuration which can immediately be identified as leading to a nonempty PDS after the remaining portion of the sentence has been processed. One can associate with each intermediate symbol the minimum number of terminal symbols required to fulfill it entirely, that is, required to eliminate entirely from the PDS the intermediate symbol itself and its new contribution of intermediate symbols to the store. In the course of analysis of a sentence, each time a new PDS configuration is formed, the simple shaper test compares the number of remaining words with the sum of such minimum numbers over all the intermediate symbols in the PDS. If the former is smaller than the latter, the rule that has produced the current PDS configuration is rejected immediately as abortive.

The generalized shaper test is basically an extension of the simple shaper

---

* Efficiency techniques described here, and a technique for repetitive path elimination described in Sec. 3 of this paper, can be applied to other context-free recognition procedures (for example, Irons' error-correcting parse algorithm[10] based on the use of a pushdown store.

test concept to include a number of specific tests on particular intermediate symbols and terminal symbols. In order for some intermediate symbols to be entirely fulfilled, certain special terminal symbols are required. For example, the intermediate symbol COMMA requires the presence of the terminal symbol "comma" in the sentence. If the PDS contains two COMMA's, and there is only one "comma" left to be processed in the sentence, the current PDS will never be emptied. The rule which produced the current PDS configuration is immediately rejected, and the analysis flow goes back to step 7 (Table 2). In the current English analyzer, generalized shaper tests are performed on the intermediate symbols COMMA ("comma"), AND ("and/or"), PA ("participle"), etc., resulting in a considerable reduction of the processing time (see Section 4 for the effect of the generalized shaper tests).

Assume that a rule has been rejected at word k due to the simple shaper or generalized shaper tests. This does not preclude, however, the use of the same rule at the same word position the next time the same intermediate symbol has become the topmost symbol in the PDS. This time, the PDS to which the new intermediate symbols of the rule are added may be such that the resulting PDS configuration may be capable of leading to an empty PDS. Therefore, the simple shaper test and the generalized shaper test apply to each use of the rule at a given word position. In contrast, consider an IC analyzer. Since a given rule at a given word position for a given length of substring in the sentence is used only once, such tests obviously cannot be and need not be invoked.

3. A Technique for Repetitive Path Elimination

As was pointed out in the previous section, the major drawback of a predictive analyzer as compared with an IC analyzer is the repetitive processing of the same substrings in the course of the analysis of a given sentence, and in connection with this problem, its incapability of identifying well-formed substrings. The new technique for repetitive path elimination which is subsequently described is a method for remedying this drawback of a predictive analyzer without introducing the problem of core storage overflow. As previously mentioned, the predictive analyzer is presently free of the problem of overflow, while the IC analyzer has to cope with it either by using an extended storage device such as magnetic tape or by abandoning the analysis. It will be shown that, according to this technique, an applicable rule at a given word position is blocked from use after the first unsuccessful attempt to employ it. Furthermore, well-formed substrings (wfs's) of various lengths corresponding to an intermediate symbol topmost in the PDS at a given word position, once identified as such, are treated as if each of them consisted of a single word. As will be shown below, the consequence of this technique is that a rule abortive at a given word position is processed no more than once, and a nonabortive rule twice, at most. The basic flow of logic for the analysis of a sentence is the same as that described in Table 2, and the new technique is superimposed on the basic flow without concern for core storage overflow.

The repetitive path eliminator uses a 72-bit *word-position register* associated with each rule in the grammar (see Table 5). Word-position registers

Table 5. Rule and Word-position Register

Rule		Word-Position Register (R)
Argument Pair, New Intermediate Symbols		
(Z, c) | $Y_1 \ldots Y_m$		1 2 3 4 k 72 0|0|1|0|...|1|...|0

are initially set to 1's for all rules in the grammar. In the course of analysis, if a given rule used at word position k for the first time turns out to be abortive, that is, to have led to no entire fulfillment of all of its new intermediate symbols, a 0-bit is stored in the kth bit position $R_k(sr(B(k)))$ of the word position register of the rule $sr(B(k))$. This 0-bit in the kth bit position prevents the use of the rule at k in any subsequent paths of analysis for this particular sentence.

Table $W(j, i)$, called "wfs length table," with 72 sets of approximately 80 72-bit registers, is used to record the lengths of identified wfs's corresponding to all the intermediate symbols at each word position. 72 is the maximum number of words in a sentence, while 80 is the approximate number of intermediate symbols currently recognized in the grammar. The ith set of registers in the wfs length table corresponds to the ith word $(i = 1, 2, \cdots, 72)$ in the sentence; the jth register $(j = 1, 2, \cdots, 80)$ in a given set corresponds to the jth member of an alphabetically ordered set of approximately 80 intermediate symbols. Since the first member of the intermediate symbol set is represented in the computer by a binary "0000001," the second member by "0000010," the third member by "0000011," and so on, the intermediate symbol itself is represented by its order in the intermediate symbol set. $W_m(j, i)$, the mth bit position ($m = 1, 2, \ldots, 71$) of the jth register of the ith set, is set equal to 1 if the jth symbol, which is topmost in the PDS at word position i, has been identified as entirely fulfillable by a wfs of length m. $W_{72}(j, i)$, originally set to zero, is set equal to 1 when the jth symbol becomes topmost in the PDS at word

Table 6. The ith Set of Registers of wfs Length Table

					mth bit					
jth symbol	1	2	3	4	5	6	7	...	71	72
0000001 (1X)	0	0	0	0	0	0	0		0	0
0000010 (33)	0	0	0	0	0	0	0		0	1
0000011 (4X)	0	0	0	0	0	0	0		0	0
1001011 (TX)	0	0	1	0	0	1	0		0	1
1001100 (UX)	0	0	0	0	0	0	0		0	1
1001101 (VX)	0	0	0	1	0	0	0		0	1
1001110 (WX)	0	0	1	0	0	0	0		0	1
1001111 (XC)	0	0	0	0	0	0	0		0	1

i for the first time. Table 6 is an illustrative layout of the ith set of registers of the wfs length table. The 1001011_2th symbol (TX) has been entirely fulfilled by a wfs of length 3 and 6; hence, 1 appears in $W_3(1001011_2, i)$ and $W_6(1001011_2, i)$. Similarly, $W_4(1001101_2, i) = 1$ since the 1001101_2th symbol (VX) has been entirely fulfilled by a wfs of length 4. $W_m(0000010_2, i) = 0$ for all the values of m and $W_{72}(0000010_2, i) = 1$ indicates that although the 0000010_2th symbol 33 has become topmost at word i, no wfs of any length has been found thus far at this word position. $W_{72}(0000001_2, i) = 0$ with $W_m(0000001_2, i) = 0$ for all the values of m shows that the 0000001_2th symbol (1X) has not become topmost in the PDS at word i yet. Given a topmost symbol $j = \alpha(i)$ at a given word position i, the register at location $(c + (80 \times 2)i + j)$ directly indicates how many wfs's of what length have been found for the symbol j, where (80×2) is the size of a set of registers for a word position and c is a constant pertaining to the address of the first location of the wfs length table.

The question, then, is how to recognize whether or not a rule has been entirely fulfilled in the course of analysis, and if so, how to identify the length of the wfs which has entirely fulfilled the rule.

It was mentioned in Section 1 that, in the predictive analyzer, at word position k in the course of analysis, the following information is available in core to identify the current path leading to k:

$A(i)$: the address of the first and the last rules of $S(i)$ for $i = 1, \cdots,$ n

$B(i)$: the address of the rule used at i, for $i = 1, \cdots, k$

$\alpha(i)$: the fulfilled intermediate symbol at i, for $i = 1, \cdots, k$

$\beta(i)$: the position, counting from the bottom, of $\alpha(i)$ in the PDS, for $i = 1, \cdots, k$

Three additional registers $\gamma(i)$, $\delta(i)$ and $F(i)$ will be added to the cycling mechanism for use by the repetitive path eliminator:

$\gamma(i)$: the word position at which $\alpha(i)$ was introduced to the PDS

$\delta(i)$: the position, counting from the bottom, of $\alpha(i)$ in the rule which introduced it in the PDS

$F(i)$: is reset to 0 when processing of $sr(B(i))$ is initiated at i and is set to 1 if a path has been found in which all the new intermediate symbols introduced by $sr(B(i))$ have been entirely fulfilled at k $(k \geq i)$

For example, if rules used at word positions 1, 2, 3, and 4 are:

1. $(X, a) \mid B\,C\,D$ 3. $(E, e) \mid \Lambda$
2. $(B, b) \mid E\,F$ 4. $(F, f) \mid \Lambda$

the registers of the cycling mechanism will contain the information shown in Table 7 (it is assumed for simplicity of illustration that the input string consists of unambiguous terminal symbols $abef \cdots$, and that there is not more than one rule in the grammar with the same argument pair).

Table 7. The Registers of Analysis Path Record for Repetitive Path Elimination

i	1	2	3	4	...
$A(i)$	[1, 1]	[2, 2]	[3, 3]	[4, 4]	
$B(i)$	1	2	3	4	
$\alpha(i)$	X	B	E	F	
$\beta(i)$	1	3	4	3	
$\gamma(i)$	0	1	2	2	
$\delta(i)$	1	3	2	1	
$F(i)$	0	1	1	1	

The entire fulfillment of the rule can be detected in the following way. When a given intermediate symbol becomes topmost in the PDS for the first time at k, all the rules belonging to $S(k)$ which have the same intermediate symbol in their argument pairs are checked one by one to see if the following condition is satisfied.

Condition 1. Is $sr(B(k))$ of the form $(Z, c) \mid \Lambda$?

If not, the normal routine (step 2, Table 2) is followed. If it is, the rule has been entirely fulfilled. Before going to step 2, $F(k)$ is set to 1, and the length of the identified wfs is recorded in the wfs length table.

In Table 7, $F(3) = 1$ and $F(4) = 1$ because the rules used at word positions 3 and 4 satisfied Condition 1. In order to identify the length of the wfs, the word position of the left-end of the wfs is stored in a register called L (for "left-end"). Since the right-end of the wfs is k, the length of the wfs is equal to $k - L + 1$. Under Condition 1, the Λ symbol was introduced to the PDS at k and was entirely fulfilled at k, so to speak. Therefore, k is stored in L, and the length of wfs $= 1$ is obtained. A 1-bit is stored in $W_{k-L+1}(\alpha(L), L)$, namely, in the first (i.e., $(k - L + 1)$-st) bit position of the $\alpha(L)$-th register at the L-th-$(L = k)$ word position. Next, a test is made to see if Condition 2 is satisfied.

Condition 2. $\delta(L) = 1$?

A fulfilled symbol at $L(= k$ initially) with $\delta(L) = 1$ (see $\delta(4)$ of Table 7) signifies that the bottom intermediate symbol of the rule used at word $\gamma(L)$ (in the example, Table 7, $\gamma(4) = 2$) has been entirely fulfilled. Therefore, the rule at word $\gamma(L)$ is entirely fulfilled. The program flags $F(\gamma(L)) = 1$ (see $F(2) = 1$ of the table) in order to indicate that the rule $sr(B(\gamma(L)))$ (i.e., rule 2 of the example above) can lead to at least one partial analysis in which all of its new intermediate symbols are fulfilled entirely. L is set to $\gamma(L)$, and a 1-bit is stored in $W_{k-L+1}(\alpha(L), L)$. Condition 2 is tested again to see if the fulfilled intermediate symbol at the new value of L is the bottom symbol of some previously used rule. This process continues until either δ of the last item flagged $\neq 1$ or $L = 0$.

When a rule at word position i has been exhaustively processed and is ready to be replaced by the next rule in $S(i)$ (see step 6 of Table 2), the content of $F(i)$ is tested. If $F(i) = 0$, the rule has never had its intermediate symbols entirely fulfilled. Therefore, a 0-bit is stored in $R_i(sr(B(i)))$, namely in the ith bit position of the word-position register of $sr(B(i))$.

In the course of analysis of a sentence, a new PDS configuration is formed at word position $k - 1$ ($k = 1, 2, \cdots, n$) as dictated by step 2 of Table 2, and the analysis flow moves to k following step 3. If k is not greater than n, a test is made to see if the topmost symbol $\alpha(k)$ has been processed previously as the topmost symbol at the same word position ($W_{72}(\alpha(k), k) = 1$?). If not, all the members of $S(k)$ have to be processed with $\alpha(k)$; therefore, step 1 is taken. On the other hand, if $\alpha(k)$ has been processed previously at k, $W(\alpha(k), k)$ is checked to see if there is any wfs corresponding to the symbol $\alpha(k)$. If there is none, the current path is abandoned, and the analysis flow goes back to the previous branching point. If there are some wfs's corresponding to $\alpha(k)$, they are processed one at a time, with $\alpha(k)$ removed from the PDS and the analysis skipped by the length m of the wfs. Such a path, when it leads to a successful analysis of the entire sentence, then contains an unanalyzed wfs of length m. In some cases, the analysis of this wfs may be found in the corresponding word positions of some previously obtained analysis of the whole sentence. In such cases, a cross reference is made to that portion (identified by word position and length) of the previous analysis (identified by analysis number) with the consequence that the rules pertaining to $\alpha(k)$ of length m are processed no more than once.

In many cases, $\alpha(k)$ of length m is not found in any of the previously obtained analyses of the full sentence.* Then, the analysis of the substring of that length is performed with $\alpha(k)$ as the initial designated symbol over all the members of $S(j)$ for $j = k, \cdots, k + m - 1$. It is at this time that word position registers R_j for the rules concerned are used in order to prohibit use of abortive rules. When a rule compatible with the current topmost symbol is found at the jth word position (step 1 of Table 2), a test is made to determine if $R_j(sr(B(j))) = 0$. If so, the rule is abortive and therefore is immediately abandoned. Since all the rules originally applicable to the current substring have already been identified as either abortive or nonabortive, no flagging of $F(j)$ is needed.

When the first analysis, for example, of "TIME FLIES LIKE AN ARROW AND THEY ARE FLYING PLANES." is obtained, all the wfs's contained in the analysis are stored in a table called *wfs reference table*. While the *wfs length table* $W_m(j, i)$ is used to store all the wfs's thus far identified, the wfs reference table is used to store only those wfs's which have appeared in some analysis of the whole sentence. Let $Q(i)$ represent the ith column of the wfs reference table. "NQ-2-1" at $Q(4)$ of Table 8,† for example, indicates that NQ is a wfs of length 2 ("AN ARROW") in Analysis Number 1. Similarly, "SE-5-1" at $Q(7)$ indicates that "THEY ARE FLYING PLANES." is identified as a wfs of length 5 in Analysis Number 1. "PD-9-1" is contained in $Q(3)$ because PD was the topmost and the only intermediate symbol in the PDS at word 3 (the sentence would have been terminated with a period at this position), and was eliminated from the PDS when the eleventh word, the period, was processed. The analysis shown in Table 8 corresponds to the interpretation of the sentence in the sense that time passes as quickly as an arrow and they are planes which are flying.

When the second analysis of the sentence is obtained in which "THEY ARE FLYING PLANES" has a structure similar to that of "the facts are

---

* This happens when the wfs of length m corresponding to $\alpha(k)$ was recognized on a path that aborted before the end of the sentence was reached.

† SE: sentence, VX: predicate, PD: period, NQ: noun object, N5: modified object, N3: noun complement, N6: modified complement, 7X: subject master, N2: object, SG: declarative clause, PA: participle.

Table 8. *The Status of* Q(i) *After the First Analysis*

i	1 TIME	2 FLIES	3 LIKE	4 AN	5 ARROW	6 AND	7 THEY	8 ARE	9 FLYING	10 PLANES	11
$Q(i)$	SE- 11-1	VX- 1-1	PD- 9-1	NQ- 2-1	N5- 1-1	PD- 6-1	SE- 5-1	VX- 3-1	N3- 2-1	N6- 1-1	PD 1-1

smoking kills," it is indicated that the analysis of the period at word 11 has been skipped because it was identified as having a wfs of length 1 (see $Q(11)$ of Table 8). The analysis of "ARE FLYING PLANES." which is the part of the sentence that has been reinterpreted, is written on the output tape with a cross reference to PD-1-1 at word 11. The length of the newly identified wfs's is computed: VX: "ARE FLYING PLANES", SG: "FLYING PLANES", and VX: "PLANES". VX-3-2, SG-2-2, and VX-1-2 are stored in $Q(8)$, $Q(9)$ and $Q(10)$ with the rightmost "2" representing the analysis number.

After the third analysis corresponding to "These people are flying (the) planes" is obtained, the program eventually "backs up" to the initial word position and processes "TIME FLIES LIKE AN ARROW" as "a species of flies called time flies are fond of an arrow." When PD becomes the topmost symbol at word position 6, $W_6(PD, 6) = 1$ indicates that a wfs of length 6 can fulfill PD entirely. Therefore, the end of the sentence is reached with an empty PDS. PD-6 is found in $Q(6)$ (see Table 8), therefore a cross reference to Analysis Number 1 is made in the analysis output record of the whole sentence. The registers of the analysis record indicate that VX at word position 3 was skipped because of a wfs of length 3: "LIKE AN ARROW". $Q(3)$ is scanned for a VX-3, but no match is found. The 3-word wfs is reprocessed with the initial symbol VX. When an analysis of the 3-word wfs is obtained, the complete analysis of "TIME FLIES LIKE AN ARROW" is given as Analysis Number 4 with a cross reference to word position 6 of Analysis Number 1 for the wfs of length 6 ("AND THEY ARE FLYING PLANES."). The wfs reference table now contains the information shown in Table 9.

The program continues its task of determining if "LIKE AN ARROW" corresponding to VX is ambiguous. When all the possible analysis branches pertaining to VX of length 3 at word 3 are exhaustively examined, the cycle is transferred back to the main analysis program, which "backs up" to word position 6, and checks to see if PD at 6 has any other wfs of

Table 9. The Status of $Q(i)$ *After the Fourth Analysis*

i	1 TIME	2 FLIES	3 LIKE	4 AN	5 ARROW	6 AND	7 THEY	8 ARE	9 FLYING	10 PLANES	11
$Q(i)$	SE-11-1	VX-1-1 7X-1-4	PD-9-1 VX-3-4	NQ-2-1 N2-2-4	N5-1-1	PD-6-1	SE-5-1	VX-3-1 VX-3-2 VX-3-3	N3-2-1 SG-2-2 PA-2-3	N6-1-1 VX-1-2 N2-1-3	PD-1-1

different length ($W_m(\text{PD}, 6) = 1$ for any m greater than 6?). Eventually, the program interprets "TIME FLIES LIKE AN ARROW AND THEY" as a compound subject as if it meant "a species of flies called time flies which are similar to an arrow, and they". Cross references are made to "VX-3-1," "VX-3-2," "VX-3-3" at word 8, and to "PD-1-1" at word 11. Finally, the program interprets "TIME FLIES" as an imperative sentence, meaning "record the time of flies," with the cross reference given to PD-9-1 at word position 3.

The repetitive path eliminator, as it is presented here, excludes the use of the number agreement test between the subject and the predicate of a sentence, and also the use of such subsidiary tests for efficiency as "simple shaper test" and "generalized shaper test." If a given rule were rejected due to any one of these tests, the rule should not be blocked from use because the same rule at the same word position while following an alternate path might enter a different PDS configuration which has a different grammatical number specification, a smaller number of intermediate symbols, or different sets of special intermediate symbols. Similarly, if one of the paths originating from a given rule were to be terminated due to any one of these tests, which is probably the case with most rules used in the course of analysis of a sentence, the rule could not be regarded as abortive because the path which was terminated might have led to the entire fulfillment of the rule if the PDS configuration had been different.

Assume, for example, that the input sentence is "A boy with a telescope and a dog are coming." and that a path corresponding to the interpretation of the noun phrase as "A boy (with a telescope and a dog)" is traversed first. When the ninth word "are" is ready to be processed, the PDS contains a singular VX as the topmost intermediate symbol. If the number agreement test were to be performed in the course of analysis, all the rules pertaining to VX and "are" would fail the test, and therefore, no wfs's corresponding to VX at word position 9 would be found. $W_m(VX, 9)$ would remain zero for $m = 1, \cdots, 71$, although $W_{72}(VX, 9)$ would be set to 1. Eventually, the analysis flow would back up and process the initial noun phrase as "A boy (with a telescope) and a dog". In this path, when "are" is ready to be processed at word position 9, the PDS would contain a plural VX as the topmost intermediate symbol. But $W_{72}(VX, 9) = 1$ and $W_m(VX, 9) = 0$ for $m = 1, \cdots, 71$ would indicate that there was no wfs found corresponding to VX at this word position. The current path would be terminated, and no analysis of the whole sentence would be obtained. Of course, it is possible to set $W_{72}(j, i) = 0$ in case a path originating from the jth intermediate symbol at word i is terminated due to a failure in the number agreement test or the subsidiary tests for efficiency, but this would have the effect of almost completely nullifying the performance of the repetitive path eliminator, because chances of one or more paths which originate from a given intermediate symbol at a given word position not being terminated by any of these tests are extremely slim. Therefore, all of these tests are inactivated in the main analysis routine. However, when a skipped wfs is reprocessed, since all the rules originally applicable to this wfs have already been identified as either abortive or non-abortive, the tests can be applied without any effect on the word position registers.

One of the advantages of the repetitive path eliminator is that, although it requires a considerable amount of core storage, the amount is still finite and of a practicable order of magnitude on an IBM 7094 computer. It will not cause core storage overflow once the wfs length table has been placed in core. The wfs reference table, although it may theoretically require an unbounded number of registers, can in practice be fairly small because the table is used to store only those wfs's which have appeared in previously obtained analyses of the whole sentence. In the current experimental program, $(77 - i)$ entries are reserved for $Q(i)$, where $i = 1, 2, \cdots, 72$. Even if the wfs reference table overflows, there is no catastrophic effect on the analysis procedure: a wfs that is to have been stored in $Q(k)$ is simply ignored. Therefore, if the same wfs appears at the same word position in a subsequent analysis of the sentence, it is not found in $Q(k)$ and therefore is reprocessed.

4. Comparison of Processing Time

An experimental program of the predictive analyzer with the repetitive path elimination is presently in operation and has well proved the efficiency of the new technique.* A routine for the number agreement test between the subject and the predicate of a sentence has not yet been incorporated; therefore, the program occasionally produces superfluous analyses which could easily be eliminated by the incorporation of such a test. Since the agreement test is to be performed only on the analyses of the whole sentence and not on all the analysis paths, the time needed for such a test is expected to be negligible. The program also does not have "simple shaper" and "generalized shaper" tests in its routine for reprocessing skipped wfs's. Such tests, when incorporated, would reduce the processing time to some degree. The performance of the "exhaustive shaper test," due to R. Abbott 11 and S. Cohen 12 and programmed by M. McAnulty, which blocks from use certain rules prior to the initiation of the predictive analysis of each input sentence, is still to be tested, in conjunction with the repetitive path eliminator. The output format for the experimental program of the repetitive path eliminator is still tentative, devised mainly for the purpose of debugging. However, it is expected that the "cleaned-up" version of the program will work as efficiently as, if not more efficiently than, the current experimental version.

The execution time of sentences processed by three versions of the Harvard English predictive analyzer is shown in Table 10. The column with the heading "1963-FJCC" shows the speed of the analyzer which was operational in 1963, described by Kuno and Oettinger 2 at the 1963 Fall Joint Computer Conference. This version of the analyzer is currently available through the SHARE Distribution Agency. The column with the heading "New SHARE" shows the speed of the new version of the analyzer which is being packaged now for submittal to SHARE. This new version is different from the previous version in that it contains the generalized shaper test and works approximately three times as fast as the previous one. The rightmost column with the heading "wfs Syntactic Analyzer" shows the speed of the experimental program of the analyzer with the repetitive path eliminator. Sentence 14, for example, which previously took 42.4 minutes and 13.2 minutes using the old and new SHARE versions, respectively, now takes 0.2 minutes (more exactly, 5.9 seconds for internal processing and 10 seconds for input/output). The 20 sentences, which used to take 87.5 minutes and 27.7 minutes, respectively, using the two SHARE ver-

---

* The author is greatly indebted to Carlton DeTar, who organized the whole program on the basis of the author's rather sketchy description 13, and to Bernard Higonnet, who continued DeTar's work and contributed to the modifications of the system. The author is also indebted to Maynard Maxwell, who programmed a routine for identifying and preventing the use of abortive rules at each word position and worked on an experimental output editing routine. All of them not only collaborated in programming and debugging, but also contributed to developing the system down to the minute details and bringing it to the current working version.

Table 10. Comparison of Processing Time of the Three Versions of the Predictive Analyzer

Sentence Number	Number of Words	Number of Analyses	1963-FJCC (min.)	NEW SHARE (min.)	wfs Syntactic Analyzer (min.)
1	17	1	0.0	0.0	0.0
2	18	1	0.1	0.1	0.1
3	25	5	1.1	0.8	0.1
4	35	12	9.0	2.2	0.1
5	16	40	0.1	0.1	0.2
6	17	4	0.1	0.1	0.0
7	14	4	0.0	0.0	0.1
8	16	3	0.1	0.0	0.0
9	23	7	0.2	0.0	0.1
10	23	31	1.5	0.4	0.1
11	30	118	7.6	3.2	0.3
12	25	72	0.5	0.5	0.2
13	32	18	9.8	3.9	0.1
14	38	94	42.4	13.2	0.2
15	25	136	7.2	0.7	0.3
16	27	1	1.7	0.3	0.1
17	30	17	1.2	0.3	0.2
18	20	71	2.7	1.8	0.2
19	29	2	1.5	0.0	0.1
20	20	16	0.7	0.1	0.1
			Totals 87.5	27.7	2.6

sions, now take 2.6 minutes, approximately two thirds of which time is for input and output.

20 Test Sentences

1. The increase in flow stress was attributed to vacancies, which have appreciable mobility at $-72°$.
2. Single strain reversals at $-72°$ not only produced the n effect but also increased the flow stress.
3. Slime formation is dependent on size of particles formed by mechanical means, amount of metal in the amalgam, and purity of solutions.
4. A shear stress applied during the recovery had no effect on the amount of recovery, if the stress was less than the instantaneous yield point, irrespective of the direction of the stress.
5. People who apply for marriage licenses wearing shorts or pedal pushers will be denied licenses.

6. Nearly all authorities agree that this will be the first practical, large-scale use of space.
7. Economic studies show that it could be a billion-dollar-a-year business by the 1970's.
8. A clutch of major companies has been pressing to get such a system into being.
9. The U.S. has reached a momentous point of decision in a project that only a few years ago would have seemed improbable.
10. Technologically speaking, there are three basic contending schemes, with a number of variations, for orbiting a communication satellite system.
11. Each of the parties to this treaty undertakes to prohibit, to prevent, and not carry out any nuclear weapon test explosion or any other nuclear explosion at any place under its jurisdiction or control.
12. This applies in the atmosphere, beyond its limits, including outer space, or under water, including territorial waters or high seas.
13. This applies in any other environment if such explosion causes radioactive debris to be present outside the territorial limits of the state under whose jurisdiction or control such explosion is conducted.
14. It is understood in this connection that the provisions of this subparagraph are without prejudice to the conclusion of a treaty resulting in the permanent banning of all nuclear test explosions, including such explosions underground.
15. Gravely concerned with spreading racial violence, President Kennedy used his press conference to issue counsel to both sides in the struggle.
16. If a farmer produces 14 bushels of oats on one acre of land, how many acres will he need to produce 700 bushels of oats?
17. A man who takes three yellow and two white capsules daily finds that a bottle of white capsules contains twice as many capsules as a bottle of yellow ones.
18. It is a mistake to think that the indeterminacy of boundaries makes our central notions less clear and valid.
19. Causes of slime formation and its reduction in the process of cementation of X by Y amalgam from Z solution containing waste from an N factory were investigated.
20. It will serve to illustrate what has been said if we apply it to the question of free will.

A corpus of 13 sentences, not listed here, which range from 40 to 56 words in length, takes 3.8 minutes for internal processing using the wfs syntactic analyzer. These are the sentences which we could not even try to analyze using either of the two SHARE versions for fear of excessive processing time.

We have operational, for the first time, a syntactic analysis system fast enough to enable us to process a large number of sentences. On the basis of studies performed on the analysis output, we can properly evaluate the performance of the current English grammar and find clues for the refinement of the grammar.

Since sentences of ordinary length can now be processed in real time, the designing of a system for information retrieval, question answering, or mechanical translation developed around the analyzer with man-machine interaction incorporated at proper places can be discussed on a practical basis.

References

1. S. Kuno and A. G. Oettinger, "Multiple-Path Syntactic Analyzer," *Information Processing 1962*, North-Holland, Amsterdam (1963).

2. S. Kuno and A. G. Oettinger, "Syntactic Structure and Ambiguity of English," *Proc. 1963 Fall Joint Comput. Conf.*, Spartan Books, Baltimore (1963).

3. S. Greibach, "Inverses of Phrase Structure Generators." Doctoral Thesis, *Mathematical Linguistics and Automatic Translation*, Rep. No. NSF-11, Harvard Comput. Lab., Cambridge (1963).

4. S. Greibach, "Formal Parsing Systems," *Comm. ACM, Vol. 7* (August 1964), pp. 499–504.

5. S. Greibach, "A new normal-form theorem for context-free phrase structure grammars." *J. ACM, Vol. 12* (January 1965), 42–52.

6. R. W. Floyd, "The Syntax of Programming Languages—A Survey," *IEEE Trans., Vol. EC-13* (August 1964), pp. 346–353.

7. D. Hays, "Automatic Language-Data Processing," *Computer Applications in the Behavioral Sciences*, Ed. H. Borko, Prentice-Hall, Englewood Cliffs, New Jersey (1962), pp. 394–421.

8. I. Sakai, "Syntax in Universal Translation," *Proc. 1961 Int. Conf. on Machine Translation of Languages and Applied Language Analysis*, Her Majesty's Stationery Office, London (1962), pp. 593–608.

9. J. Robinson, "Preliminary Codes and Rules for the Automatic Parsing of English," RM-3339-PR, RAND Corp., Santa Monica (December 1962).

10. E. T. Irons, "An Error-Correcting Parse Algorithm," *Comm. ACM, Vol. 6* (November 1963), pp. 669–673.

11. R. Abbott, "An Exhaustive Shaper Test as Preliminary Analysis Technique," *Mathematical Linguistics and Automatic Translation*, Sec. IX, Rep. No. NSF-13, Harvard Comput. Lab., Cambridge (1964).

12. S. Cohen, "Application of the Exhaustive Shaper Test as Preliminary Analysis Technique," *Mathematical Linguistics and Automatic Translation*, Sec. X, Rep. No. NSF-13, Harvard Comput. Lab., Cambridge (1964).

13. S. Kuno, "New Techniques for Repetitive Path Elimination," *Mathematical Linquistics and Automatic Translation*, Sec. XI, Rep. No. NSF-13, Harvard Comput. Lab., Cambridge (1964).

7 Connectability Calculations, Syntactic Functions, and Russian Syntax

David G. Hays

1. Introduction

When a PL (parsing logic) routine selects a possible combination of occurrences, it transfers the combination, with descriptions of their syntactic properties, to a CT (connectability test) routine. This routine, using a concrete grammar of the language in which the text is written, determines whether the properties of the occurrences and the general rules of the grammar permit the combination. The CT routine returns a yes-or-no answer; or, if such concepts are used by the grammarian, a measure of the probability, value, or utility of the combination. In its most general form, a CT routine is capable of supplying more than one positive answer for a single combination. Different dependency directions (cf. Sec. 1.2) or different functions (cf. Sec. 2) may have to be distinguished. As a byproduct of the connectability test, the CT routine furnishes, for every positive answer, a description of the syntactic properties of the new composite.

Both PL and CT routines can be designed in many ways, given the same linguistic theories and facts. The CT routine to be presented here is to be used with a general PL routine; the combination, given a grammar and text, will find every grammatically allowable structure for the text (but whether any of those structures is valid or intuitively acceptable depends on the content of the grammar). For use with a PL routine intended to produce the most "probable" structure of an input string, the CT routine would have to be modified, but only slightly, and in fact the designs of the two parts of a sentence-structure determination program are almost independent.

Note: The work reported here was accomplished in part at The RAND Corporation and completed at the Common Research Center of the European Atomic Energy Community, Ispra, Italy, while the author was a Stagiaire qualifié there on leave from RAND. Reprinted (abridged) with permission from *Mechanical Translation*, Vol. 8, No. 1 (August 1964), pp. 32–51.

1.1. Code Matching CT Routines

The classic format for a grammar is a construction list. Each entry has three or more parts, naming the construction and each of its members. The connectability-test routine required is a table-lookup routine; the descriptions of two or more occurrences are looked up in the list, and if the combination is found the name of the construction it forms is found with it. This format is somewhat inconvenient in practice for two reasons. First, if the name of a construction is a concatenation of its syntactic properties, then it often resembles the name of one of its members (the governor). Space in the table is therefore wasted by repetition within each of many entries. Second, the linguist faces a dilemma. If just one symbol is assigned to each distinct unit, the number of rules is increased because many classes of units can participate in unique sets of constructions. If many symbols are attached to each distinct unit, the list can be greatly shortened, but the number of references to be made during sentence-structure determination is increased.

Code-matching CT routines as a class are distinguished by the fact that they require no list of constructions.1 The syntactic description stored with each occurrence is in a format and notation that permits direct calculation of connectability and of the properties of the combination if one is permitted. In principle, the latter calculation can require the storage of considerable information that is not usable until the combination is formed. Code matching CT routines are related to the formal systems known as categorial grammars,2 which are known to have essentially the same power as context-free phrase-structure grammars,3 hence of dependency grammars.4 In a categorial grammar, each syntactic description is a string of symbols containing one special mark. The string to the right of that mark is matched with the entire string characterizing a following unit, and the two units are connectable if and only if the two strings match exactly. In important papers on the subject, these strings are constructed with two primitive symbols (s = sentence, n = noun), parentheses, and the special mark. As a result of these restrictions, on the matching process and on the alphabet of symbols, the syntactic descriptions needed for natural language are formidable, and the number of different strings assigned to each distinct occurrence is large. Linguistically, it seems more convenient to use both a more elaborate matching process and an enlarged alphabet. In the Russian example given below, the size of each syntactic description is large but limited, not subject to indefinite growth, and most Russian items can apparently be characterized syntactically with a single description.

The principle used here is the isolation of *syntactic functions* and *agreement variables*. On the order of a dozen functions are proposed for Russian;

every syntactic relation between a pair of occurrences in a Russian text is to be regarded as an instance of exactly one function. An occurrence is characterized by the functions it can enter and by values of the agreement variables. Each function entails agreement with respect to certain variables. The CT routine therefore seeks a function common to a pair of items and then tests their agreement with respect to the variables material to that function. (In this paper, *material* will be used in this sense; a variable is material to a function if the function entails agreement with respect to it.)

1.2. Dependency and Projectivity

The theory of categorial grammars imposes an asymmetry on every construction. Let / be the special mark, and let s/n be the description of a transitive verb. Then when a noun (description n) follows a transitive verb, the matching operation (symbolized by a dot) gives s/n.n = s. Part of the symbol of the verb remains, whereas the symbol of the noun has entirely disappeared. In general, a code-matching system can be devised to retain parts of both symbols, but a rule of *pars major* can be invoked to maintain the asymmetry. Moreover, the special mark can be regarded as dividing each grammatical symbol into a part to be matched with a dependent and a part to be matched with a governor. Thus the articulation of dependency theory with code matching is natural. In particular, any function must be regarded as asymmetrical, *served by* one occurrence, *governed by* another, even if phrase structure theory is adopted.

The theory of dependency will be assumed here, and with it the continuity rule of projectivity. The PL routine is therefore supposed to furnish combinations of occurrences consisting of adjacent unit occurrences or adjacent composites whose heads (principal members, from which all other unit occurrences depend directly or indirectly) are to be joined directly by dependency. If the heads of two composites (or two unit occurrences, or a unit occurrence and a composite) are identified as X and Y, the CT routine tests whether X can depend on Y and gives a yes-or-no answer; it also tests whether Y can depend on X, and gives a separate answer to that question.

1.3. Unit Occurrences

It is assumed here that the units identified during dictionary lookup are *forms,* simultaneously the largest units constructable by morphological rules and the smallest units to which syntactic descriptions can be assigned. This separation of morphology and syntax is justified, linguistically, on three grounds; the argument applies to Russian and presumably to certain other languages, but certainly not to all natural languages. First, the categories and construction rules of Russian morphology and syntax are separable with virtually no overlap (i.e., morphological rules are exocentric). Note here that the categories needed in morphological rules and the categories established by morphological properties are not necessarily identical; many syntactic properties of Russian forms are established by their morphological constitution. Second, an absolutely strict size-level distinction can be made between morphology and syntax, so that dictionary lookup of forms can be completed before sentence structure determination, using only syntactic rules, begins. Third, the continuity rules for morphological and syntactic constructions are somewhat different and much simpler if separated. Specifically, the continuity rule for morphological constructions is that the immediate constituents of each construction are continuous (with some notable exceptions), whereas the rule for syntax is projectivity. Projectivity does not seem to hold in Russian if the syntactic unit is taken to be the morph or morpheme. Incidentally, forms are bounded by spaces or marks of punctuation in printed Russian text and only a limited number of forms or morphological construction types contain either spaces or marks of punctuation. Those containing spaces are strictly limited, and those containing punctuation—mainly the hyphen— are of limited types although not limited in number. The same is true of many other printed languages. Another separation satisfying these three criteria (separability of rules, separability by size level, and simplification of continuity rules), or even the first two, does not appear to exist in Russian but might well appear in English, for example.

2. Functions

The code matching plan to be described here can be used with any set of functions, or varieties of grammatical relationships. Let us assume that the functions of a language have been determined; then each unit, elementary or composite, is characterized by two lists of functions: those it can govern and those it can serve as dependent. A description of the structure of a sentence will specify, for each elementary unit, what function it serves in the sentence and what occurrence governs it. For example, in "John ate breakfast" the unit occurrences are "John", "ate", and "breakfast". Here "John" serves subjective function, governed by "ate"; "breakfast" serves objective or complementary function, also governed by "ate"; and "ate" itself serves predicative function, with no governor.

The functions of a language can be classified as optional or singular. An optional function is one that can be served by any number of dependents of a given occurrence; for example, the function of adjectival modifiers of nouns in English may be optional. A singular function is one that can be served by at most one dependent of a given occurrence, such as the subjective function in various languages. (If two conjoined nouns, or two nouns in apposition, serve as subject of a Russian or English verb, the function is nevertheless served only once, by the conjoint or apposite group.) A singular function is said to be obligatory if it must be served by a dependent of every occurrence of a given unit.

Ignorance of empirical fact could lead an investigator to classify two singular functions together as one optional function. This error is corrigible, however, since an occurrence capable of governing both of the singular functions can govern only one dependent with each of them, a fact that can be revealed by study of texts and interrogation of informants. The differentiation of adjective order classes in English, for example, may lead to identification of several singular adjectival functions in place of the optional function now hypothesized. Any two singular functions can be reduced to one if no occurrence in the language is capable of governing both, but cannot be if some occurrences govern one dependent with each function. On the other hand, all of the optional functions of a language can be taken as a single function, since—by definition—governing one dependent with an optional function does not prevent an occurrence from governing others.5

Statements about functions governed and functions served determine the major form classes of a language. These necessarily supersede all other part-of-speech classes, which would be irrelevant for syntactic operations. A syntactic unit, elementary or composite, is primarily characterized by three lists of functions: those it can govern, those it must govern, and those it can serve as dependent. This set of three lists is called the *function triple* of the item. A major form class consists of all forms bearing identical function triples. Within a form class, the agreement variables that are material for any of the functions mentioned differentiate the class members.

Agreement variables are *material* for a function if two units connected with that function agree with respect to that variable. The notion of agreement to be understood here is very broad; it covers the agreement of Russian adjectives with the nouns they modify, and also the agreement between a verb that requires an accusative object and the accusative noun depending on it. The agreement requirements of a function are *homogeneous* if the same agreement variables are material for every combination of units connected with the function. If the modifying function in Russian is a single, optional function, its requirements are heterogeneous, but it can be analyzed into two subfunctions with homogeneous requirements: adjectival and adverbial. The complementary functions in Russian are heterogeneous; many Russian forms can govern as complement either a noun or a noun clause, with different agreement requirements in the two situations (the noun must be in a certain case, the noun clause must be introduced by a certain conjunction). On the other hand, if a unit can *serve* complementary function, the material variables are always the same for it; hence minor form classes can be identified.

Under certain circumstances it is necessary to assign two or more function triples to a single unit which therefore belongs to two or more major form classes and can be called *homographic*. Let $F_1, F_2, \ldots, F_n$ denote the functions of a language. There are four cases.

1. If unit X can serve some F_i only in occurrences in which it also governs some F_j, and if F_j is not obligatory for X, then X is homographic. For example, finite forms of the Russian *byt'* $= be$ can serve predicative function, but only if they govern complements. Otherwise they serve only auxiliary functions, and do not govern complements. One function triple allows X to serve F_i and makes F_j obligatory; another does not allow X to serve F_i and either omits government of F_j or makes it singular.

2. If X can govern F_i only if it simultaneously governs F_j, then X is homographic. Its two function triples are similar to those described under (1), *mutatis mutandis*. Any Russian infinitive can be regarded as homographic for this reason; it can govern a subject only if it governs an auxiliary. (But this can be taken as an example of exocentrism; see below.)

3. If X cannot govern F_i and F_j simultaneously, even though in general they can be governed together, then X is homographic. (If the two kinds of dependents could not be governed together by any unit in the language, they would be identified as the same function.)

4. If the value for X of some agreement variable material to function F_i, which X can serve or govern, varies according to the nature of the dependent that serves function F_j for X, then X is homographic; likewise, of course, if the mere presence of a dependent with function F_j is influential. For example, the presence of a negative modifier as dependent of an ordinary transitive verb influences the properties of the direct object permitted in Russian. With the negative modifier, a verb that normally governs the accusative can instead govern the genitive.

As a rule, the functions of a governor are not modified by the attachment of a dependent; when modification takes place, we can speak of *exocentrism*. Exocentrism and homography are to some degree interchangeable. Economy helps to determine which facets of linguistic structure will be handled by one device, which by the other. Consider case 1, as described in connection with homography. Since, in a projective language, it is always possible to attach all dependents to a unit before attaching the unit to its governor, the conditioning dependent can always be attached before the conditioned. Case 2 is different, since projectivity does not guarantee that the conditioning dependent is attached first; that depends on the grammar of each language individually. If the class of units that can serve the conditioning function is small, and the class of homographic units would be large—as with infinitives (a large conditioned class) and auxiliaries (a small conditioning class)—it is more economical to mark the conditioning units and revise the function triple of the governor when the dependent is attached, provided that the order of attachment can always put the alteration ahead of the pertinent test.

Functions can be classified as coordinative and dominative. The agreement requirements of coordinative functions are symmetric in the sense that the same agreement variables are tested for both members of the pair of associated units. In general, two units can be coordinated if there is some function that the two can serve jointly, but the details are complicated and cannot yet be discussed clearly. Dominative functions are all the others. In Russian, there appear to be at least two coordinative functions, conjunction and apposition, with more than one kind of conjunction possible. The rest of this section treats the dominative functions of Russian.6

The dominative functions currently hypothesized for Russian are subjective, complementary (three functions), auxiliary (three functions), modifying and predicative. The following illustrations are archetypal:

Subjective function: Nominative noun depending on finite verb.

First complementary function: Accusative noun depending on finite verb, *or* genitive noun depending on noun.

Second complementary function: Dative noun depending on verb.

Third complementary function: Prepositional phrase depending on verb.

First auxiliary function: Finite verb (small category) depending on infinitive verb, *or* finite form of *byt'* depending on short-form adjective.

Second auxiliary function: Negative particle *ne* depending on verb.

Third auxiliary function: Comparative marker depending on adjective.

Modifying function: Adjective depending on noun, *or* adverb depending on verb.

Predicative function: Finite verb depending on relative adverb.

The subjective, complementary, auxiliary, and predicative functions are singular. For the present, the modifying function is optional, and it remains to be seen whether an economical classification of modifiers would lead to a set of singular or obligatory functions to replace this one.

3. Design of a Code Matching CT System

To simplify the exposition of the agreement variables, the general plan of the CT system in which they are to serve is presented first. According to this plan, a grammar-code symbol is assigned to each form in the dictionary and attached to each form occurrence in text during dictionary lookup. Each symbol consists of a string of binary digits (1's and 0's) of fixed length. The nth digit has a certain linguistic significance, and the format of the grammar code symbols is a statement, for each position, of its significance. Each position represents one value of a variable with respect to some operation in the CT routine. For example, if grammatical case is a variable, a noun can be characterized with respect to case in more than one way: its own case, as determined by its ending; the case it governs (usually genitive); and so on. A set of positions representing all the values of one variable will be called a *frame*. A frame, filled with digits characterizing a form with respect to a definite operation, occupies a certain set of positions in the grammar-code symbol, and that set of positions will be called a *segment*. One frame is needed for the set of syntactic functions named above. It has nine positions, for which abbreviations will be used: subjective (s), first complementary (c^1), second complementary (c^2), third complementary (c^3), first, second, and third auxiliary (x^1, x^2, and x^3, respectively), modifying (m), and predicative (p). This frame applies to three segments of the grammar-code symbol: functions governed (F_g), functions served as dependent (F_d), and functions governed obligatorily (F_o). To refer to a segment of the grammar-code symbol of an occurrence, we will use the name of the segment and the location of the occurrence. Thus $F_g(A)$ is the functions-governed segment of the symbol attached to the occurrence at location A in a text. When it is necessary to refer to a single binary position in the grammar-code format, we will use abbreviations for variable values as superscripts: $F_g{}^s$, for example, refers to the subjective-function position of the functions-governed segment, and $F_o{}^{x^3}$ to the third-auxiliary position of the obligatory-functions segment.

The first step in the comparison of two grammar-code symbols is to determine whether there is any function that one can serve for the other. Call the two occurrences D and G, and assume that the test is restricted to determining whether occurrence D can serve any function for occurrence G. If $F_g{}^i(G) = 1$, then occurrence G can govern a dependent with function i (here i stands for any function). Likewise, if $F_d{}^i(D) = 1$, occurrence D can serve function i. If there is some function i for which $F_d{}^i(D) = F_g{}^i(G) = 1$, then occurrence D can serve function i for occurrence G, provided that the agreement requirements of function i are satisfied. The Boolean product, $F_g(G) \& F_d(D) = F$, is constructed by setting $F^i = 1$ if $F_g{}^i(G) = F_d{}^i(D) = 1$, and writing $F^i = 0$ otherwise. This product can be obtained easily and very quickly by most modern computers, for long strings of 1's and 0's.

Boolean products, also called logical products, will be used throughout this CT routine. In several instances below, it is sufficient to characterize the product as equal to zero or not. If the product F defined above equals zero, occurrences G and D cannot be connected with G as governor; otherwise, their connection is subject to further tests. For functions, and also in several instances below, it is necessary to determine the locations of all 1's in the product. Thus, for functions, each function has its own agreement requirements, and the further tests to be performed follow those requirements. The exact form of the *functions test* is:

Test $F_g(G)$ & $F_d(D) = F$.
If $F = 0$, stop.
Otherwise, if $F^i = 1$, test agreement with respect to function i.

The tests for the separate functions will be described below. This statement of the test can be encoded for operation on a computer, given the length of F and the fact that F can contain any combination of 1's and 0's.

Another operation, the Boolean or logical sum, will be needed. The sum of X and Y, $X \vee Y = Z$, is defined by: $Z^i = 1$ if $X^i = 1$ or $Y^i = 1$, and $Z^i = 0$ otherwise. Thus $Z^i = 0$ if $X^i = Y^i = 0$. The sum of two segments therefore marks the properties possessed by either of two items.

4. Grammar-Code Symbol Format

The format used here for Russian grammar-code symbols has 38 segments using 11 frames. One frame, for syntactic functions, has been described. The others are substantive type (T), nominal properties (N), clause type (K), prepositional phrase type (H), first auxiliary type (X_1), modifier type (M), preceding adverbial type (D_1), following adverbial type (D_2), location (L), global type (G), and global nominal properties (J).

4.1. Substantive Type

Four syntactic functions are served by substantives (the subjective and complementary functions). The units that can serve these functions are diverse, and any governor of a substantive function imposes certain limits on the variety of units that it accepts. Classifying these units according to further agreement requirements, they are nominals (n), infinitives (i), clauses (k), prepositional phrases (h), and adjectivals (a).

Nominals are nouns (morphologically defined) and items that can replace nouns in all contexts: substantivized adjectives, pronouns, relative pronouns, cardinal numbers, etc. These units must satisfy agreement requirements with respect to case, number, gender, person, and animation— the *nominal properties* described in Sec. 4.2.

Infinitives, defined syntactically, are the same items as if they were defined morphologically.

Clauses are sentences marked by conjunctions, relative pronouns, or relative adverbs and capable of serving substantive functions. Of course, not every Russian clause is substantival.

Prepositional phrases consist of prepositions with their complements and occurrences that derive from the complements, but only those that serve complementary functions are marked in the substantive-type frame.

Adjectivals are long-form instrumental adjectives, a few genitive nouns, and certain other items that replace long-form instrumental adjectives in copula sentences.

The grammar-code symbol of a form includes five segments to which this frame applies. One describes the unit coded (T_d), one indicates the type of subject governed by the unit coded (T_{gs}), and three describe the types of complements governed by the unit coded, one each for first, second, and third complements $(T_{gc1}, T_{gc2}, T_{gc3})$.

When the connectability of two items is tested, if the functions test shows that occurrence D can serve a substantive function (say first complementary) and that occurrence G can govern it, the substantive types of G and D are compared: $T_{gc1}(G)$ & $T_d(D)$. It follows that if $F_g{}^{c1} = 0$ for some item, then the content of T_{gc1} for that item is linguistically immaterial, and can have no influence on any connectability test involving the item.

Similar statements can be made about all other segments of the grammar-code symbol; each is material for an item only if definite preconditions are satisfied.

The segments indicating type of substantive governed can obtain any possible pattern of 1's and 0's, since, for example, a verb may exist that governs, as second complement, any subset of the set of substantive types. On the other hand, T_d never contains more than a single 1; no Russian item is ambiguously either a prepositional phrase or a subordinate clause. Hence the product of T_d with one of the T_g's never contains more than a single 1. In this the substantive-type test differs from the functions test, and the difference is large from the programming viewpoint.

4.2. Nominal Properties

The variables ordinarily discussed in Russian grammars as characterizing Russian nominals are person, number, gender, case, and animation. The subject of a Russian verb ordinarily must agree with respect to all of these except animation (and Harper 7 shows that verbs taking animate and inanimate subjects can be differentiated). The complement of a verb, noun, or preposition must be in a certain case, or possibly in one of a few selected cases. A noun and any adjective modifying it must agree in number, gender, case, and animation.

The patterns of ambiguity generated by Russian morphology make these variables interdependent. Thus case and number are tied together by such forms as *linii,* which is genitive singular, nominative plural, or accusative plural. This form cannot be characterized simply as nominative, genitive, or accusative, as singular or plural, since that would imply that it can be genitive plural. Either two separate descriptions—two grammar-code symbols—must be assigned to the item or case and number must be combined and treated as a syntactic variable with twelve values, three true for the example. The latter course is preferable, because it accelerates sentence-structure determination with only a small increase in storage requirements (or even, perhaps, with a saving). All five nominal properties are interdependent in this sense.

Taking the simplest view, the complex nominal properties variable would have 216 values. For number has two values, gender three, case six, person three, and animation two: $2 \times 3 \times 6 \times 3 \times 2 = 216$. Note, however, that gender is neutralized in the plural, that person (material only for the subjective function) is neutralized except in the nominative case, and that animation (disregarding Harper's finding for the moment) is material only in the accusative case. Combining number and gender into a variable with four values—masculine (m), feminine (f), neuter (n), and plural (p)—and combining case, person, and animation into a variable with nine values—nominative first person (n_1), nominative second (n_2), nominative third (n_3), genitive (g), dative (d), accusative animate (a_a), accusative inanimate (a_n), instrumental (i), and prepositional (p), the complex variable has 36 values: masculine nominative first person (mn_1), masculine nominative second person (mn_2), and so on, through plural prepositional (pp). The fact that nominal properties can be represented with a 36-valued variable is obviously related to the fact that certain computers use a 36-position storage cell. If larger cells were available, the nominative third person could well be differentiated into animate and inanimate, adding four values to the complex variable.

The nominal properties frame N, with 36 positions, applies to five segments of the grammar-code symbol: N_d, N_{gs}, N_{gc1}, N_{gc2}, and N_{gc3}, for description of the item itself, of the subject governed by the item, and of the first, second, and third complements governed by the item. These segments are used in tests for subjective and complementary functions if the dependent is a nominal-type substantive. In the test of modifying function, if the modifier is adjectival type, $N_d(G)$ & $N_d(D)$ is examined; this is the outstanding exception to the rule that *different* segments of the grammar-code symbols of governor and dependent are involved in each connectability test.

4.3. Location

A frame with two positions is used to specify the relative location in text of governor and dependent. The first position is for dependent before governor, the second for governor before dependent. The frame is denoted L, its positions L^1 and L^2. In grammar code symbols, this frame indicates restrictions on order. If a governor can have either a preceding or a following dependent, l's appear in both positions, but if the governor must follow, there is a l in the first position only. The frame applies to six segments in the grammar code symbol: L_{gs}, L_{gc1}, L_{gc2}, L_{gc3}, L_{da}, and L_{dx}. The first refers to the subject governed by the coded item, the second, third, and fourth to the complements it governs, the fifth to its own location as adjectival dependent, and the last to its own location as auxiliary. The frame also applies to a segment not in the dictionary but constructed when two occurrences are to be tested for connectability. This segment, always containing a single l, indicates whether the occurrence being considered as potential governor lies before or after the other. It is denoted L_t.

4.4. Global Properties

Global properties are those that belong to any phrase, up to a certain syntactic type, that contains an item bearing the property. For the present, two such properties are known. The word *li* anywhere in a sentence makes the whole sentence interrogative; a sentence containing *li* can serve as a subordinate clause with substantive function. The word *kotoryj* anywhere in a sentence marks it as an adjectival subordinate clause. The two positions of G, the global properties frame, are denoted G^i (*li*-clause) and G^a (adjectival clause). Only one segment is needed for global properties, showing the global properties of the entire construction headed by the occurrence coded. In the dictionary, G is blank for every form except *li* and the forms of *kotoryj*.

4.5. Global Nominal Properties

A Russian adjectival clause must agree with the noun it modifies with respect to only two variables: gender and number. Some forms of *kotoryj* are ambiguous with respect to these variables, and since these variables are interdependent with case, the ambiguity can sometimes be resolved when *kotoryj* is attached to a governor in the subordinate clause. The global nominal properties of a subordinate clause, or of any construction within a subordinate clause that contains *kotoryj* are the gender and number of the antecedent expected. The frame has four positions (masculine, feminine, neuter, and plural) and applies to one segment, J, which is always blank in the dictionary and filled out when the governor of *kotoryj* is found.

[The descriptions of the other frames are omitted.]

5. The Connectability Test Routine

From a strictly formal point of view, it is possible to construct an algorithm for testing connectability in any language with context-free phrase-structure grammar. The simplest version of the algorithm supposes that each grammar code symbol is divided into two parts, one showing what "functions" the item can govern, the other what "functions" it can serve as dependent. To test a pair of items, the algorithm merely matches the government code symbol of one with the dependency code symbol of the other. Even with isolation of syntactic functions and agreement variables, as proposed here, a universal algorithm is possible. It would require, for each language, a reference table entered with the name of a function and containing an indication of the segments of the two grammar code symbols to be matched. One line of the table, for Russian, would be

$$Fx^1 : X_{1g}(G) \& X_{1d}(D)$$

where the left-hand symbol, denoting a function, labels the entry, and the right-hand part, the entry proper, shows what parts of the grammar code symbols are to be tested. The tests for several Russian functions are more complex, however. Given the modifying function, the first step is to test type; then, if adjectival, to test nominal properties and, if adverbial, to test adverbial type. Such processes can be described in table entries, but they are more readily presented in the form of a program. Since the universal program is absolutely trivial, the only complexity is in the concrete detail of a particular grammar, and it seems convenient to surrender universality for the sake of having a more powerful tool for the description of individual grammars.

The general form of the routine is universal. First, there is a test for possible functions. For each possible function, there is a subroutine. If the agreement requirements for the function are homogeneous, the material segments are tested by taking a logical product which is zero or nonzero. If zero, the items cannot be connected with that function; if nonzero, they can be. If the agreement requirements for the function are heterogeneous, a test to determine type of agreement requirement intervenes and can give one of several answers: no connection possible, or else a certain type of agreement to be tested, implying certain segments as before. In principle, a sequence of type, subtype, subsubtype, etc., tests could be required before specification of agreement variables, but the sequences found in Russian are short. Besides tests of segments of grammar code symbols, tests of relative location are included in the present routine, and tests of punctuation could be added.

Before the CT routine is applied to a pair of occurrences, the parsing logic routine has selected them in accordance with its design and their place in the sentence, has designated one of them as potential governor, and has produced $L_t(GD)$, a location segment showing whether the governor or dependent lies ahead of the other in test. The steps in the routine are named for convenience and numbered for reference.

1. Function Selector

Test $F_g(G)$ & $F_d(D) = F$.

If F $\quad = 0$, stop.
If $F^s \quad = 1$, test subjective function (2).
If $F^{c^i} = 1$, test i-th complementary function (3^i).
If $F_x{}^1 = 1$, test first auxiliary function (4).
If $F_x{}^2 = 1$, test second auxiliary function (5).
If $F_x{}^3 = 1$, test third auxiliary function (6).
If $F^m \quad = 1$, test modifier function (7).
If $F^p \quad = 1$, test predicative function (8).

The test produces the logical product of $F_g(G)$ and $F_d(D)$ and examines it. If all positions are zero, the routine is stopped and the PL routine seeks another pair; this is the meaning of "stop" throughout the CT routine. Otherwise, all of the nonzero positions are noted and for each some operation is performed. These operations cannot be performed in parallel, but it is best to imagine them as simultaneous. Each uses the grammar-code symbols supplied for occurrences D and G by the parsing-logic routine and each does or does not produce an output independently of all the others. When one of these routines produces an output, it alters certain portions of the grammar-code symbol of G, but these alterations do not affect either the original symbol on which the other routines are working or the symbols that they will produce as output. It would be possible, in principle, for the CT routine to yield nine separate outputs, and it will not be rare for it to produce two.

2. Subjective Function

Test $L_{gs}(G)$ & $L_t(GD) = L$.

If $L = 0$, stop.
If $L \neq 0$, test subjective substantive type (2.1).

This test controls relative location of G and D. In a nominal sentence, where the predicate is headed by a noun in the nominative case, either the first nominative noun in the sentence or the second could be regarded as the subject. If $L_{gs} = 10$ for every noun that can govern a subject, the first will always be taken as subject, eliminating an ambiguity that seems universal and pointless.

2.1. Subjective Substantive Type

Test $T_{gs}(G)$ & $T_d(D) = T$.

If T $\quad = 0$, stop.
If $T^a = 1$, test subjective nominal properties (2.2).
If $T^k = 1$, test subjective substantive clause type (2.3).
If $T^i = 1$, prepare output for subjective function (2.5).

The subject of a Russian sentence is a nominal, a clause, or an infinitive. Since T_d contains at most a single 1, this test leads either to a stop or to exactly one branch. If the possible subject being tested is nominal or an infinitive, further tests must be performed, but no further agreement requirements are known for infinitive subjects.

2.2 *Subjective Nominal Properties*

Test $N_{gs}(G)$ & $N_d(D) = N$.

If $N = 0$, stop.

If $N \neq 0$, replace $N_{gs}(G)$ with N and prepare output for subjective function (2.5).

There may be several 1's in N, but they have no functional significance. The remaining ambiguity in the nominal properties of the subject are irresolvable syntactically, since the subject already has all of its own dependents. The nominal properties of the subject, were their ambiguities resolved one way or another, would not influence the connectability of any other occurrence with the governor of the subject. Hence it is not necessary to produce multiple outputs, one for each possible resolution of the ambiguities remaining. (In this the agreement variables contrast with syntactic functions.)

2.3. *Subjective Substantive-Clause Type*

Test $K_{gs}(G)$ & $K_d(D) = K$.

If $K = 0$, stop.

If $K \neq 0$, test clause-subject location (2.4).

This test determines whether the substantive clause proposed as subject is of a type that can be accepted by the proposed governor. Remaining ambiguity is immaterial, hence there is no branching on type of clause. If it should prove to be the case, however, that different types of clauses have different location rules, then a branching would be necessary.

2.4. *Clause-Subject Location*

Test $L_{ds}(D)$ & $L_t(GD) = L$.

If $L = 0$, stop.

If $L \neq 0$, replace $K_{gs}(G)$ with K, from (2.3), and prepare output for subjective function (2.5).

In 2 above, a test for location requirements of the governor was made. Here the location requirements of the dependent are examined.

2.5. *Output for Subjective Function*

Set $F_g{}^s(G) = 0$.

$F_d(G) = 000\ 000\ 001$.

$T_{gs}(G) = T.$
$D_{1g}(G) = D_{1g}(G) \text{ v } D_{1g}(Pred).$
$D_{2g}(G) = D_{2g}(G) \text{ v } D_{2g}(Pred).$

Do global properties routine (9).

The governor, since it has a subject, cannot have another; the function is singular. The governor, since it has a subject, cannot serve any function but the predicative. Altering $T_{gs}(G)$ here completes the marking of G to show exactly what type of subject it governs; if the subject is nominal, $N_{gs}(G)$ was altered in 2.2, and if it is clausal, $K_{gs}(G)$ was altered in 2.4. Since G must serve predicative function, it can govern any adverbial modifier that modifies all predicate heads (such as the sentence modifiers that sometimes introduce Russian sentences). The predicate modifiers are described by $D_{1g}(Pred)$ and $D_{2g}(Pred)$, which are stored as part of the CT routine and incorporated in the adverbial-type government segments of G by logical summation. The complete output, to be finished by the parsing-logic routine, will include the occurrence numbers of G and D, note that G is governor, and that D serves subjective function.

[Other tests are omitted.]

9. *Global Properties*

Test $G(D) = G.$

If $G = 0$, stop.
If $G^a = 1$, do global nominal-properties routine (9.1).
If $G^i = 1$, prepare output (9.3).

A zero result means that the dependent, whether intrinsically or as a result of previous attachment of some deeper dependent, has no global properties. If $G^a = 1$, either the dependent in the newly-formed connection is a form of *kotoryj,* or it governs, directly or indirectly, some form of *kotoryj.* Likewise, $G^i = 1$ indicates the presence of *li.*

9.1. *Global Nominal Properties*
Test $J(D) = 0.$

If yes, do determination of global nominal properties (9.2).
If no, prepare output (9.3).

For every entry in the dictionary, including *kotoryj,* J is blank. This segment is filled out only by the application of 9.2. Hence if $G^a(D) = 1$, and $J(D) = 0$, then D is an occurrence of *kotoryj.*

9.2. Determination of Global Nominal Properties
Test $N_d(D) \& N(Masc) = N$.
If $N = 0$, do (9.2.1).
If $N \neq 0$, set $J^m(G) = 1$ and do (9.2.1).

9.2.1. Feminine
Test $N_d(D) \& N(Fem) = N$.
If $N = 0$, do (9.2.2).
If $N \neq 0$, set $J^f(G) = 1$ and do (9.2.2).

9.2.2. Neuter
Test $N_d(D) \& N(Neut) = N$.
If $N = 0$, do (9.2.3).
If $N \neq 0$, set $J^n(G) = 1$ and do (9.2.3).

9.2.3. Plural
Test $N_d(D) \& N(Plu) = N$.
If $N = 0$, prepare output (9.3).
If $N \neq 0$, set $J^p(G) = 1$ and prepare output (9.3).

These four tests are used to reduce the 36-position segment $N_d(D)$ to the 4-position segment $J(G)$. $N(Masc)$, $N(Fem)$, $N(Neut)$, and $N(Plu)$ are four nominal-properties segments stored with the CT routine and containing 1's in their masculine-singular, feminine-singular, neuter-singular, and plural positions, respectively.

9.3. Output for Global Properties
Set $G(G) = G(D)$.

With this step, carrying forward the global properties of the dependent as the global properties of the new governor, the global-properties routine and the CT routine are complete and the parsing-logic routine can begin its search for a new pair of possibly connectable occurrences.

Punctuation, not discussed here, is used to facilitate or prevent connections. It is also used to mark occurrences or connected sequences of occurrences that can serve as appositives or as adjectival dependents of preceding governors. And, in addition, punctuation is used to close off sentences and clauses. When a connected sequence, surrounded by appropriate punctuation, is found to be headed by an occurrence that can serve predicative function, the sequence is regarded as an independent sentence. With different boundaries and a head occurrence that can serve predicative function and is marked with global properties, a connected sequence is regarded as a subordinate clause and given a new grammatical description permitting it to serve as adjectival-modifying dependent or as clausal-substantive dependent.

6. Morphology and Syntax

Terse summaries of morphology and of syntax, each taken separately, tend to be quite short. The brevity of this paper, although it is quite incomplete, is at least suggestive. The statement of Russian syntax included here consists, in fact, of the format in Sec. 4 and the CT routine in Sec. 5. To be added are routines (more than one will be needed) for coordinative functions and, very likely, additional steps in the routine of Sec. 5 for tense sequence, inter-complementary agreements, and so on. Even with these additions, the whole statement of Russian syntax would be extremely short, and corresponding statements of morphology (i.e., of construction rules that apply within the form) are of similar length. Whether statements about higher strata (transformational or sememic statements) can be equally short is unknown, but they may well be. The ease with which natural languages are learned makes their simplicity almost certain—at least their simplicity in certain senses.

There remains the fact, however, that standard treatises on the grammars of modern languages are large and dense with detail. This detail seems mostly to concern interstratal relationships, and that fact is worth noting as a guide to future research. The syntactic behavior of morphologically defined categories is studied, and morphologically unusual items are analyzed, syntactically, one by one. Since not all syntactic properties can be derived from morphological properties, sememically defined categories are also considered. This plan of presentation, although often somewhat confusing because the morphologico-syntactic correlations are often confounded with the sememo-syntactic correlations, has merit.

Suppose that the complete description of a language, beyond the phonological or graphic stratum, consists of formats and CT routines for morphological, syntactic, and sememic levels (not strata, since morphology and syntax belong to one stratum), together with a dictionary and rules for interlevel conversion. Suppose, furthermore, that the CT routines and formats are all simple. The conversions may not be. Syntactic grammar-code symbols for forms have to be obtained as the end product of a dictionary-lookup operation that may involve a morpheme list and a CT routine; syntactic properties then have to be ascribed to stem morphemes, affix morphemes, and their constructions. Design of a good routine for this purpose calls for exactly the kind of information supplied, with more or less precision and accuracy, in large grammars. The syntactic-to-sememic conversion, since it crosses a stratal boundary, calls for another dictionary lookup, and semotactic code symbols may have to be obtained as the end product of operations with another CT routine. Despite the grammars, the amount of such information still to be collected and systematized can hardly be exaggerated.

7. Acknowledgments

The author is indebted to K. E. Harper, C. F. Hockett, M. J. Kay, Y. Lecerf, S. L. Marks, B. Vauquois, D. S. Worth, and T. W. Ziehe for the benefit of their criticisms and suggestions.

References

1. Code-matching techniques were suggested by A. F. Parker-Rhodes, "An Algebraic Thesaurus," presented at an International Conference on Mechanical Translation, Cambridge, Massachusetts (October 15–20), 1956. Ariadne Lukjanow, then at Georgetown University, used the term to apply to a method that she proposed, and Paul Garvin (of Bunker-Ramo, Inc.) has developed a system, somewhat different from that proposed here, for Russian syntax.

2. J. Lambek, "The Mathematics of Sentence Structure," *American Mathematical Monthly*, Vol. 65, No. 3 (1958), pp. 154–170.

3. Y. Bar-Hillel, C. Gaifman and E. Shamir, "On Categorial and Phrase-structure Grammars," *Bulletin of the Research Council of Israel, Section F*, Vol. 9, No. 1 (1960), pp. 1–16.

4. H. Gaifman, "Dependency Systems and Phrase Structure Systems," P-2315, The RAND Corporation (1961).

5. *Cf.* the discussion of strong and weak government in L. N. Iordanskaya, *Two Operators for Processing Word Combinations with "Strong Government" (for Automatic Syntactic Analysis)*, Moscow (1961). Translated in JPRS 12441, U.S.. Joint Publications Research Service (1962).

6. *Cf.* Hockett's discussion of "Construction Types"; C. F. Hockett, *A Course in Modern Linguistics*, Macmillan (1958), pp. 183–208.

7. K. E. Harper, *Procedures for the Determination of Distributional Classes*, RM-2713-AFOSR, The RAND Corporation (1961).

8 The Grammar of Specifiers

David A. Dinneen

Editor's Comment: Dinneen's thesis treats French grammar in the way
V. H. Yngve suggested in "A Model and an Hypothesis for Language
Structure" (*Proceedings of the American Philosophical Society*, Vol. 104,
No. 5 [October 1960], pp. 444–466). He produces sentences under the
control of a phrase-structure grammar, but with some special devices.
Each symbol carries *subscripts* denoting values of grammatical variables;
in the expansion of a symbol, subscript values are automatically carried
along. The production mechanism starts with a symbol, expands it into a
string, expands the leftmost nonterminal in the string, and so continues
until a string of terminals has been constructed. If each terminal is emitted
as soon as possible, so that only nonterminals have to be stored, this plan
tends to keep storage requirements small.

But the production mechanism is segmented, in an uncommon way,
into a producer of *specifiers* and a producer of sentences operating under
partial control of the specifiers. The first segment is described in the parts
of the thesis reprinted here: Chapter 4 (pp. 39–46), Appendix II-C, and
Appendix IV.

1. Introduction

The Grammar of Specifiers is a routine which is executed prior to the
Grammar of Sentences each time a clause (independent or dependent) is
to be generated. As each rule in this routine is executed, specific decisions
are made about the nature of the clause, and appropriate subscripts are
added to the symbol that represents the clause in the program. These subscripts are later used to delimit choices in rules within the Grammar of
Sentences, rules which cannot be chosen completely at random because of

Note: This work was performed in the Mechanical Translation Group, Research
Laboratory of Electronics, Massachusetts Institute of Technology, with support in
part by the National Science Foundation, the United States Army Signal Corps, the
Air Force Office of Scientific Research, and the Office of Naval Research; computer
time was provided by the Massachusetts Institute of Technology Computation Center.
This excerpt from the author's thesis, "A Left-to-Right Generative Grammar of
French" (December 1962), is reprinted with permission.

the decisions made in the Grammar of Specifiers. They are transferred, when appropriate, to the constituent members of this clause as it is expanded.

The decisions regarding the basic characteristics of the clause are made before the symbol for it is expanded, rather than at various points during the actual generation of the clause, because they affect the word order to such an extent and in such a way, that postponement of the decisions would result in placing extreme limits on the possible sentences to be generated, preventing the generation of certain types altogether. This appears to be analogous to the way in which the human speaker formulates his sentence, that is (1) he decides upon certain aspects of the sentence; (2) then he chooses the sentence-type (word order); finally (3) he utters the specific words. The aspects of the sentence that I have included in the Grammar of Specifiers are

1. The choice among the interrogative, declarative and imperative types of sentences.
2. How to signal the interrogative and, when necessary, the choice of the other syntactic function of the interrogative word.
3. The choice between the affirmative and negative and, if a negative sentence is to be generated, the choice of the other syntactic function(s) of the negative particle(s).
4. The choice between the active or passive voice, and, if passive, whether or not the agent will be expressed.

I first decided to construct and study a "Grammar of Specifiers" principally to help me in programming the grammar. In the earliest versions of the grammar-program, I found that many of the errors in the sentences being generated could have been avoided if certain general, high-level decisions had been made earlier in the program. My procedure in constructing the Grammar of Specifiers was to add one unit at a time as the need for it appeared in the print-out of sentences. I have, in fact, considered a number of other decisions that could be made in the specifier routine which would simplify the programming of the main grammar. However, I have included in this version of the grammar only those decisions that I consider basic and necessary parts of a Grammar of Specifiers, specifically those that cannot be restricted to a single constituent and that radically affect word order. My reason for not including the other aspects in the Grammar of Specifiers is that although I believe that the most important criterion to use in judging the value of a given section of the generative grammar is whether or not it functions well, I am also anxious to consider the apparent analogy between the Grammar of Specifiers in my generative grammar and some similar component or activity in the mind of the human speaker. I did not feel that the aspects I decided against including in the Grammar of Specifiers were likely to be considered in advance by the human speaker, despite the fact that, for the computer program, it was definitely much simpler to consider them before the actual generation of the sentence.

The importance of the Grammar of Specifiers can be seen in its application to mechanical translation research as well as to research in general syntax. It is of particular interest in mechanical translation because it suggests a means of defining, developing, and manipulating "specifiers" in the translation process. As decisions are made in the Grammar of Specifiers routine about certain aspects of the sentence to be generated, appropriate subscripts are added to the symbol representing the sentence constituent. The subscripts are the specifiers of the sentence. In a translation process, the specifiers of the sentence to be generated would be provided by the "translation step." The analysis of the original sentence (in the input language) would have produced the set of specifiers of the sentence. Then, rather than translating at the word level, or even at the level of syntactic structures, we would translate at the more abstract level, the specifier level. The resulting translation would be an equivalent set of specifiers in the output language, which would control the operation of the generative grammar, producing a sentence in the output language.

Taking just one aspect, the interrogative, of a simple sentence, I shall try to illustrate the steps described above. I am to translate the English sentence, "Is John sick?" into French. The first component analyzes the English sentence, producing a set of specifiers. One of these specifiers notes that the sentence is interrogative. (Others note that "John" is the subject, that the tense is present, that the verb is copulative, and so on.) After translation, the French set of specifiers still includes the fact that the sentence is interrogative, but it is also noted (because there is a noun subject and because of the absence of any interrogative adverb, particularly of the class to which *où* belongs) that inversion of the subject and verb is not possible. The generative grammar is permitted to choose between two word order types: using *est-ce que* plus normal word order, or using a pleonastic subject pronoun. Thus the output sentence could be either, *Est-ce que Jean est malade?* or *Jean est-il malade?* That is, the specifiers do not necessarily specify particular structures and forms that must be chosen, but rather they specify the *limits* set on the grammar to produce a sentence that is syntactically equivalent to the sentence in the input language. I feel that the study of the use of subscripts in the Grammar of Specifiers in my program will help me to develop a more concise notion of the nature of "specifiers" in the mechanical translation scheme I have just outlined.

One of the ways the Grammar of Specifiers may be applied to research in general syntax would be to utilize the fact that it can control choices in the grammar of sentences in order to effect a limited study of a particular type of structure. For example, if I wished to study *faire* causal constructions and others which influence word order, it would be simpler both to add the structure at the Grammar of Specifiers level and also to test the new structure in actual runs of the program, rather than to add or alter many rules at various points in the main program. Ideally, the rules of the Grammar of Sentences should be complete and general enough to produce all combinations of structures. The Grammar of Specifiers must control the execution of the rules in the Grammar of Sentences in order to prevent the generation of ungrammatical combinations.

2. Description of the Grammar of Specifiers in the Program

The Grammar of Specifiers is a complete, organized set of rules that is used over and over again. It is called a routine in the programmed grammar. The following verbal description of the Grammar of Specifiers is intended to explain generally what the routine does and, to some extent, how the operations are executed. I believe that it illustrates sufficiently the function of this important routine in the complete program. However, I have also provided (in Sec. 3) a complete and more detailed description of the entire routine, by means of a step-by-step diagram.

In the Grammar of Specifiers routine (Fig. 1), the first decision, which the machine is free to make at random, is "What basic type of sentence will be generated?" If it is to be declarative or interrogative, a choice is made about the voice (active or passive) and then, after further decisions are made about the interrogative sentence, the computer program goes on to decide if the sentence will be affirmative or negative. If at the first step it was decided that the sentence would be imperative, the computer immediately decides whether or not it will be an affirmative imperative sentence. If affirmative, there are no further decisions to be made and control passes to the Grammar of Sentences. If negative, the symbol for this negative imperative sentence is then operated on by the same set of rules regarding negative choice as operate on the symbols for declarative and interrogative sentences.

For both declarative and interrogative sentence types, if the sentence is to be affirmative, no further questions are asked and control passes to the Grammar of Sentences. This step was taken separately for the imperative type sentences because of the unique word order rules for the affirmative imperative. For all three basic sentence types, if the sentence is to be negative, a set of decisions must be made about the syntactic function of the negative particle(s) before control can pass out of the Grammar of Specifiers.

For interrogative sentences, the questions and subsequent restrictions on

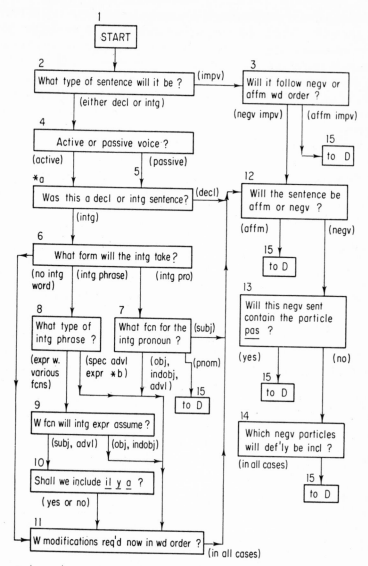

*a In the program this is not a separate step, therefore no reference number is given for the step-by-step description.

*b That is, the type that causes inverted word order.

NB The numbers at each box correspond to the numbers in the step-by-step description in sec. 3. Reference D is in the Grammar of Sentences.

Fig. 1. Grammar of specifiers.

rules as indicated by the subscripts are concerned with the *form* of the interrogative (type of word or expression, inversion, or use of *est-ce que*), and the *function* of any interrogative word or expression. Following these decisions, the computer must choose the basic word order of the sentence.

As each of the decisions outlined above is made, a subscript is added to the symbol that is destined to be expanded into a string of syntactic structures and finally into a string of words, forming a sentence. The symbol will carry the subscripts and transfer them, as required, to each and every constituent that is generated by the grammar of sentences during the expansion of the sentence or clause under consideration. Then, whenever a rule is to be executed that is affected by one of these subscripts, the computer is directed to choose the subrule indicated by the subscript.

The following simple example illustrates how the decisions made in the Grammar of Specifiers affect operations in the Grammar of Sentences. In the Grammar of Specifiers, the machine chooses to generate an affirmative imperative sentence. Later, in the Grammar of Sentences, when the PREDI-CATE constituent is to be expanded, the computer is limited (by the subscripts transferred to that constituent from the original SENTENCE constituent) in its choice of subrules. It cannot choose to expand PREDI-CATE into INDIRECT-OBJECT-PRONOUN plus VERB-WITH-ITS-COMPLEMENTS in that order. Furthermore, when VERB-WITH-ITS-COMPLEMENTS is to be expanded, the computer is again limited to choices which do not include the generation of a pronoun direct object in front of the verb. The verb, when it is expanded, cannot be analytic, and so on. Each of these restrictions is noted as a subscript and when and if the pertinent constituent is to be expanded, the calculator refers to the subscript before executing the expansion.

3. Details of the Routine

1. Initialization.

Clear dispatcher of all entries. Reset dispatcher with subscripts on the symbol now in the workspace (symbol for sentence, relative clause, etc.). ((GO TO 2))

2. What basic type of sentence shall we generate?

a. Declarative: Set subscripts for indicative mood, period as end punctuation; any conjoined independent clause must also be declarative. ((GO TO 4))

b. Interrogative: Set subscripts for indicative mood, question mark as end punctuation; any conjoined independent clause must also be interrogative. ((GO TO 4))

c. Imperative: Set subscripts to produce PRED only, for imperative mood, synthetic verb form, exclamation point as end punctuation, person-number at either 2nd singular or plural or 1st plural; any conjoined independent clause must be imperative. ((GO TO 3))

3. Will this imperative sentence be negative or affirmative?

a. Affirmative: Set subscripts for affirmative predicate, restrict PRDB and VCMP, prohibit generation of a verb modifier, set a "switch" showing this is an affirmative imperative clause. ((GO TO 15))

b. Negative: Set subscripts for negative predicate, prohibit generation of a negative subject. ((GO TO 12))

4. Will the sentence be active or passive?

a. Active:
   (1) and it will be declarative (noted at 2)—((GO TO 12))
   (2) and it will be interrogative (noted at 2)—((GO TO 6))

b. Passive: Set subscripts to restrict VCMP expansion to either VBMD or VBMD + CMPINF (no VBOB permitted); set ISPV and PSV "switches" to show this is a passive sentence, thereby assuring generation of a transitive verb and correct ordering of the elements of the verb phrase (particularly in case of imbedded negatives). ((GO TO 5))

5. Will the agent be expressed or not?

a. Yes: Set PRDA to generate an agent.
b. No: No operation required (PRDA is normally set at *no* agent).
*—for both a. and b.: if sentence is to be decl, GO TO 12.
                 if sentence is to be intg, GO TO 6.

6. What form will the interrogative take?

a. Interrogative pronoun: Set subscripts to assure entry into interrogative word routine in the Grammar of Sentences (*before* expanding SENT into SUBJ + PRED), also to assure choice of an intg pro. ((GO TO 7))

b. Interrogative phrase: Set subscripts as for a., except final choice here is set for an interrogative expression. ((GO TO 8))

c. No interrogative word: *Est-ce que* still permitted. No operation. ((GO TO 11))

7. What function will the interrogative pronoun form assume?

a. Subject: Set subscripts to produce subject form of *lequel* or *qui*, to generate PRED only, and to prohibit generation of a negative subject. ((GO TO 12))

b. Object: Set subscripts to produce object form of *lequel* or *qui*, to prohibit generation of a negative object, to choose the zero form of the direct object in usual position, to prohibit choice of word order which permits SUBJ + PRED plus an inserted pleonastic pronoun subject form (that is, *not Que le prof. dit-il?*, but *Que dit le prof.?*), to assure that VCMP and VBOB go through usual VB + OBJ routines. ((GO TO 11))

c. Indirect Object: Set subscripts to produce indirect object forms of *lequel* or *qui*, to prohibit generation of a negative particle functioning as indirect object, to account for usual indirect object routines in the predicate. ((GO TO 11))

d. Adverbial: Set subscripts to produce adverbial constructions with *qui* or *lequel*. No other restrictions. ((GO TO 11))

e. Predicate Nominative: Set subscripts to produce predicate nominative forms of *lequel* or *qui*, to account for the predicate nominative routines in the predicate, generating a zero form in the usual position ((GO TO 7.1))

7.1. Which of the two following word order types is to be used for the predicate nominative construction?

a. Expand SENT to PRED only, but provide for the VRBSUB pleonastic subject pronoun (here, of course, *not* pleonastic). ((GO TO 15))

b. Inverted (PRED + SUBJ) order. ((GO TO 15))

8. What type of interrogative phrase will it be?

a. Adverbial of type 1, that is, which *permits* inversion of the subject *noun* and predicate: Set subscripts to assure choice of a type 1 interrogative adverb, to leave word order choice free. ((GO TO 11))

b. Adverbial of type 2, that is, which does not permit inversion of subject noun and predicate: Set subscripts to assure choice of a type 2 interrogative adverb. ((GO TO 11))

c. An expression with various possible functions. ((GO TO 9))

9. What function will the interrogative expression assume?

a. Subject: (Subscripts are set here as they were in 7 for each function.) ((GO TO 10))

b. Object: ((GO TO 11))

c. Indirect Object: ((GO TO 11))

d. Adverbial: ((GO TO 10))

10. Shall we insert *il y a*?

No operations. Still to be programmed. ((GO TO 11))

11. What modifications in word order are now required and/or permitted, in consideration of any interrogative constructions that are to be generated?

Note: The rule is normally set to prohibit the choice of subrules d and e. They are only possible under certain conditions which may be developed in the preceding operations.

a. Normal word order plus *est-ce que*: Set subscripts to assure generation of *est-ce que* and to assure expansion of SENT to SUBJ + PRED. ((GO TO 12))

b. Inversion of verb with pronoun subject. No noun subject expressed: Set subscripts to assure generation of a "pleonastic" subject pronoun, to expand SENT to PRED only, and to prohibit generation of a negative particle functioning as the subject. ((GO TO 12))

c. Inversion of verb with pronoun subject. Noun subject *is* expressed: Set subscripts to assure generation of a pleonastic subject pronoun, to expand SENT to SUBJ + PRED and to prohibit generation of a negative particle functioning as the subject. ((GO TO 12))

d. Inversion of verb with noun subject: Set subscripts to expand SENT to PRED + SUBJ, to assure generation of a synthetic verb form, to prohibit generation of a negative particle functioning as the subject. ((GO TO 12))

e. Leave word order unchanged. ((GO TO 12))

12. Will the sentence be affirmative or negative?

a. Affirmative: No operations. ((GO TO 15))

b. Negative: Set subscripts to assure generation of a negative particle *ne* at the head of the PRED. ((GO TO 13))

13. Will this negative sentence contain the particle *pas*?

a. Yes: Set subscripts to assure generation of a verb modifier (the modifier must be negative, specifically *pas*), to assure that the verb form, if analytic, will be discontinuous and, if a passive construction is formed, it also must be discontinuous. ((GO TO 15))

b. No: Set subscripts to assure that, if a negative verb modifier is generated, it will not be *pas* and to permit optional generation of other negative particles (initially prohibited). ((GO TO 14))

14. Which of the possible negative particles shall we definitely choose to be generated? We have decided to make the sentence negative, and have provided for a *ne*, but have chosen not to generate a *pas*. We must therefore be sure to generate at least one other negative particle.

Regardless of the one we choose here, the choice of additional negative particles remains optional.

a. Subject: Set subscripts to assure generation of a negative subject. ((GO TO 15))

b. Object: Set subscripts to assure generation of a negative object, via restricted expansion of VCMP and VBOB. ((GO TO 15))

c. Indirect Object: Set subscripts to assure generation of a negative indirect object, via limited expansion of PRED. ((GO TO 15))

d. Verb Modifier: Set subscripts to assure generation of a negative verb modifier. ((GO TO 15))

e. Predicate Modifier: Set subscripts to assure generation of a negative predicate modifier. ((GO TO 15))

f. Participle Modifier: Set subscripts to assure generation of a negative participle modifier and to assure that the verb form will be analytic and non-discontinuous. (The "participle modifier" was added to the program for research purposes only. I do not consider it an integral part of the program-grammar.) ((GO TO 15))

15. End of the Grammar of Specifiers. Go on to the Grammar of Sentences.

9 Research Methodology for Machine Translation

H. P. Edmundson and David G. Hays

1. Introduction

This paper is the first of a series that describes the methods now in use at The RAND Corporation for research on machine translation (MT) of scientific Russian. The limitation to scientific text results from the importance of prompt, widespread distribution of Soviet scientific literature in the United States. The purpose of this series is to clarify the technical problems of computer application in linguistic research, to stimulate research in machine translation, and to encourage standardization of working materials. The present paper describes the general approach being followed, giving its philosophy and method.

The *general approach* used at The RAND Corporation for conducting research on MT is that of convergence by successive refinements. At each stage, automatic computing machinery is used for some aspects of translation, and for collecting and analyzing data about other aspects.

The *philosophy* that underlies this approach is empirical, in the sense that statistical data are collected from careful translations of actual Russian text, analyzed, and used to improve the MT program. Preconceptions about language are generally suppressed in this approach; no attempt is made to create a complete linguistic theory in advance. Nevertheless, cogent formalizations and previous knowledge of language are adopted whenever they seem useful.

The *method* is conveniently divided into four components:

1. *Text Preparation.* Russian scientific articles are pre-edited and punched into a deck of IBM cards.

Note: This research was sponsored by the United States Air Force under Project RAND—Contract No. AF 49(638)-700 monitored by the Directorate of Development Plans, Deputy Chief of Staff, Research and Development, Hq USAF. Reprinted from *Mechanical Translation*, Vol. 5, No. 1, (July 1958), pp. 8–15, with the permission of authors, publisher, and The RAND Corporation.

2. *Glossary Development.* A second deck is punched, including a card for every different "word" in the text. Some pertinent linguistic information is added.

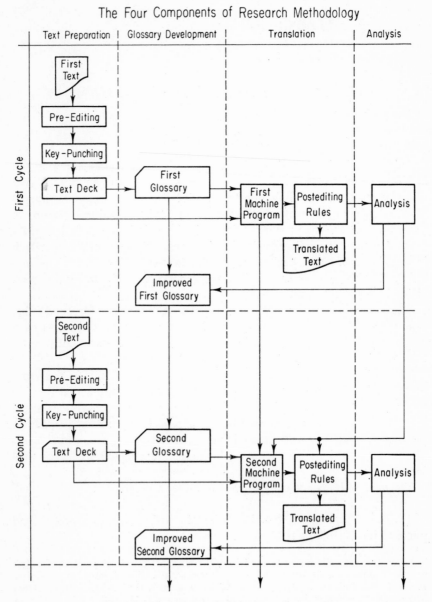

The Four Components of Research Methodology

Fig. 1. Flowchart of the research process.

3. *Translation.* Using the glossary, an IBM 704 program produces a rough translation of the text. This translation is postedited.

4. *Analysis.* The postedited translation is studied in order to improve the glossary and the machine-translation program.

These four components of the research method are described in some detail in the present paper. However, a complete exposition is contained in the RAND Studies in Machine Translation, Numbers 3 through 9.

2. Text Preparation

The preparation of a corpus of Russian scientific text on punched cards involves selection of articles, pre-editing, design of machine codes and card formats, and keypunching.

2.1. Selection of Articles

The present RAND corpus consists of articles in the fields of physics and mathematics. These fields were chosen because of their importance for national security, and also because of the fact that their reputedly limited vocabularies assure a slow rate of glossary increase, which is useful in the preliminary cycles of research. A bibliography of the current RAND corpus is contained in MT Study 9.*

2.2. Pre-Editing

Pre-editing is necessary for efficient keypunching; decisions are made before the keypunch operation begins, so that the operator knows exactly what to punch and in what order. The variety of characters and arrangements that is possible on a printed page cannot be reproduced on a standard keypunch machine. The pre-editor substitutes, for each nonpunchable symbol or formula, a code that can be punched. He assigns an index number to each article; to each page of the article; to each line of the page; and to each occurrence in the line. The current rules for pre-editing are contained in MT Study 4.†

2.3. Machine Codes

American punched-card machinery is not designed to process the Cyrillic alphabet; modifications are required, either in equipment or in procedure.

---

* K. E. Harper, D. G. Hays, and B. J. Scott, "Studies in Machine Translation: Bibliography of Russian Scientific Articles," RAND Memorandum RM-3610-PR, The RAND Corporation (June 1963).

† H. P. Edmundson, D. G. Hays, E. K. Renner, and D. V. Mohr, "Studies in Machine Translation—4: Manual for Pre-editing Russian Scientific Text," RAND Memorandum RM-2065-1-PR, The RAND Corporation (June 1961). [But see also Chapter 3 in this volume.]

For the present, it is most convenient to adapt procedures. Accordingly, three distinct codes for the Cyrillic alphabet are needed:

a. *Keypunch Code.* Special key-tops are prepared for the Cyrillic alphabet, and arranged on the keyboard of an IBM Type 026 keypunch in the pattern of a standard Russian typewriter. Each letter of the Cyrillic alphabet is punched into cards with a unique combination of holes, but these combinations are not adapted to machine sorting or listing.

b. *Sort Code.* The standard construction of IBM card sorting and collating machines defines a natural ordering of certain punch combinations. The RAND sort code assigns these punch combinations to the Cyrillic characters in their natural order. Thus it is possible, using standard IBM machines and standard procedures, to sort cards into Cyrillic alphabetic order.

c. *List Code.* The letters of the Roman alphabet, decimal digits, and a few special characters can be printed on IBM equipment. Each of these characters is printed by a unique punch combination. The RAND list code causes IBM equipment to print a Roman transliteration of the Cyrillic original. The transliteration used here was designed for convenient machine printing.

Of these three codes, the sort code seems most reasonable as a permanent, standard IBM code for Cyrillic characters. In the first place, the "natural" order of the punch combinations is related to the arrangement of punches in the card column, as well as to the construction of sorters and collators. Furthermore, the sort code uses one column for each Cyrillic character, whereas the list code requires as many as four columns for phonetic representations of some characters.

The keypunch code can be eliminated by mechanical alteration of the keypunch. The list code can be eliminated by construction of type wheels with Cyrillic characters for the machines used in listing. In the absence of special equipment, use of three distinct codes is unavoidable; conversions among the codes are most conveniently performed on an automatic computer.

3. Glossary Development

In accordance with the general approach of this project, the glossary is developed by increments. An initial glossary is prepared from a small corpus; examination of a new corpus leads to expansion of this glossary; and so on. Initially, the rate of growth of the glossary is large; as the process continues, the rate will decrease, but never vanish.

During each cycle, the new corpus is alphabetized on the Russian form.

A summary deck is produced, containing one card for each different form; the number of occurrences of each form is recorded in this process. The new summary deck is mechanically matched with the old glossary, and new forms are listed for coding by linguists.

The linguist adds information to the new glossary cards as follows:

a. *Grammar Code.* Each form is coded for part of speech, case, number, gender, tense, person, degree, and so forth. The current RAND code has more than 1,000 categories; it is described in MT Study 6.*

b. *Word Number.* Each form in the corpus is numbered automatically; it remains for the linguist to collect all inflected forms of a single word and assign a number identifying the group as a word.

c. *English Equivalents.* If the new form is a form of a word in the old glossary, the English equivalents previously used are carried forward. If no form of the word has occurred before, the linguist assigns up to 3 tentative English equivalents. His selection may be altered after postediting. (See Analysis.)

Grammar code, word number, and English equivalents are keypunched into the summary cards and then transferred to the translation text cards.

4. Translation

From one point of view, almost the whole research process consists of translation. In a stricter sense, however, "translation" is used to describe the two-stage process of machine translation and postediting. The process begins with the translation text deck, already containing glossary information and sorted into textual order. A 704 program produces a listing of the text as a rough translation; a posteditor works on this list, converting it into a smooth English version of the Russian original. The object of this process is to produce Russian-English translations suitable for the analyses described in the following section.

4.1. Machine Translation

The 704 computer program for MT will eventually determine the structure of Russian sentences and construct equivalent English sentences. The program is expanded and improved as cycles of research produce more information about language, so it is impossible to give a final description of it. During the first cycle, the "machine-translation" program consisted solely of transliteration of the text and printout of the glossary information.

---

* K. E. Harper, D. G. Hays, and D. V. Mohr, "Studies in Machine Translation—6: Manual for Coding Russian Grammar," RAND Memorandum RM-2066-1-PR, The RAND Corporation, (December 1960).

Analyses in the first cycle have led to the following machine routines, completed or planned:

a. *Recognition of Idioms that Have Previously Occurred.* An idiom is a sequence of forms that must be translated as a group, not one-by-one. This routine is ready for the second cycle.

b. *Inflection of Nouns into Plural Number.* The English equivalents in the glossary are generally uninflected. Hence it is necessary, when a Russian noun occurs in plural number, to inflect its English equivalent into the plural. A fairly complete routine is ready for the second cycle, but it does not take into account the fact that some forms of Russian nouns are ambiguous with respect to number. Extensions of the routine are planned to be in operation in the second cycle; these will use adjective-noun agreement to reduce the ambiguities.

c. *Inflection of Verbs by Voice, Mood, Tense, Person, and Number.* In English the inflection of verbs is more complicated than that of nouns. The third-person singular present tense, the past tense, the present participle, and the past participle require inflections; at times, auxiliary verbs and pronoun subjects also must be inserted. A routine to handle many inflections is planned to be in operation in the second cycle, but insertion of pronoun subjects in particular must wait for further textual analysis.

d. *Insertion of Prepositions.* When a Russian noun occurs in the genitive, dative, or accusative case, its English equivalent must, in most instances, be preceded by a preposition. The Russian noun may or may not be preceded by a preposition. A routine is planned to be in operation during the second cycle, which will connect Russian prepositions with their noun objects and will supply additional prepositions in English as required.

e. *Selection of English Equivalents for Russian Prepositions.* Russian prepositions have many alternative English equivalents. K. E. Harper, using the postedited corpus from the first cycle, has developed a classification of nouns that improves the accuracy of preposition translation. A routine is planned to be in operation during the second cycle, to select an equivalent for each preposition according to the class of the noun to which it is connected.

The computer program for machine translation has thus advanced since the first cycle began, but must be improved in every respect before machine translation is satisfactory without postediting.

The machine-translation stage concludes with the printing of a *text list.* The following items are printed in parallel columns:

> sequence number—coding space—
> Russian form—grammar code—
> primary English equivalent—
> alternative English equivalents

The primary English equivalent, copied from the glossary in the first cycle, is to be modified by the machine-translation program in subsequent cycles.

The text list is designed to serve three different functions; its format economically provides for the support of these tasks:

a. *Evaluation of the Machine-translation Program.* The quality of the program can be judged by reading the primary English equivalent column.

b. *Postediting.* The posteditor, who must know both English grammar and the subject matter of the article, can work from the English equivalents and the grammar code; he has no occasion to refer to the glossary. His notations are marked directly in the coding space; the text list then serves as a keypunch manuscript.

c. *Linguistic Analyses.* The same list can be used by a linguist for structural or other analyses of the text.

4.2. Postediting

The posteditor inserts whatever notations are required to convert the rough machine translation into good English; his notations are analyzed in order to improve the glossary and the computer program. It is thus necessary for him to have good command of English grammar and the technical vocabulary of the scientific articles being translated. His task is to complete the work of the machine, so the rules he follows must change from cycle to cycle as the machine-translation program develops. The following rules apply in the second cycle:

a. *English Equivalents.* The primary English equivalent is generally acceptable (see the following section, Glossary Refinement); if it is not, the posteditor makes one of three notations:

(1) He writes the code number of a listed alternative English equivalent in the coding space.
(2) He writes a new alternative English equivalent in the coding space.
(3) He writes a special symbol to denote that a string of occurences is an idiom.

In one of these ways, the posteditor makes sure that the selected English equivalent is always acceptable in the context.

b. *English Sentence Structure.* The structure of the sentence is partially converted to English style by the machine-translation program; as that program develops in repeated cycles of research, fewer and fewer structural notes have to be made by the posteditor. Among his tasks are these:

(1) Inflection of English equivalents, or correction of the inflections made by the machine program.
(2) Insertion of English preposition codes when necessary, or correction of insertions made by the machine program.

(3) Insertion of codes giving correct English word order.

By such notations as these, the posteditor guarantees that the final product is grammatically acceptable in English.

c. *Russian Sentence Structure.* The posteditor indicates the connections in the sentence that makes up its structure. Using such rules as the following, he writes next to each occurrence the sequence number of the occurrence on which it depends:

(1) Adjectives depend on the nouns they modify.
(2) Nouns that serve as objects of prepositions depend on the prepositions.
(3) Nouns that serve as subjects or objects of the verbs depend on the verbs.
(4) Words connected by conjunctions depend on the conjunctions.

The posteditor continues until every occurrence in the sentence, except one, is shown to depend on some other.

The selection of English equivalents and synthesis of English sentence structure was performed by the posteditor in the first cycle. Machine determination of Russian sentence structure is being initiated for the second cycle. The current rules for postediting are contained in MT Study 8.*

5. Analysis

The final component of this research methodology is analysis of the postedited translation, with the goal of refining both the glossary and the computer program. Some analyses are performed at the conclusion of each cycle; the advantages of this method include the following:

1. Compared with the preparation of a "complete" MT program before examination of any corpus, this method is more closely governed by the realities of language.

2. Compared with the translation of a very large corpus before any analysis or programming, this method is less costly, since it makes more efficient use of the posteditor's time. It is possible, by means of analyses in early cycles, to shift part of the work of corpus preparation from the editor to the computer program in subsequent cycles.

It follows that the two chief criteria for selection of analyses in each cycle are rapid reduction of the posteditor's work and selection of a corpus for each analysis large enough for statistical stability. Language problems that most often arise tend to satisfy both criteria in early cycles.

---

* H. P. Edmundson, K. E. Harper, D. G. Hays, "Studies in Machine Translation—8: Manual for Postediting Russian Scientific Text," *Mechanical Translation,* Vol. 6 (November 1961), pp. 63–71.

The method of analysis is empirical correlation of the posteditor's notations with the information in the glossary—word number, grammar code, and so forth. The following paragraphs describe some applications of the method.

5.1. Glossary Refinement

In each cycle, the glossary is enlarged by the addition of new forms and new idioms. In addition, analysis leads to improvement of the English equivalents. It is first necessary to determine, for each Russian word (i.e., set of forms) the minimal set of English equivalents required. The determination is made in the following steps:

1. A count is made of the number of occurrences for which each alternative equivalent is preferred by the posteditor. The alternatives are rearranged in the glossary in order of frequency of preference.
2. In subsequent cycles, the posteditor is instructed to accept the first alternative as often as possible.
3. Secondary alternatives that are not preferred in subsequent cycles are deleted.

The English equivalents that remain are essential for accurate translation; thus it is necessary to develop criteria for choice of one of them in each context. The first task is to differentiate between the contexts in which a multiple-equivalent word is translated in different ways. The analytic text deck contains one card for every occurrence, and, after postediting, each card is punched to show the English equivalent, and the words in the context summarized and tabulated. Presumably there are words that occur more often in the context of one preference than of the others; if such words exist, they permit differentiation of the contexts.

At least two more cycles are required before the RAND corpus will be large enough for this type of analysis. If, at that time, the data show strong differentiation of contexts, it will be necessary to construct models. One model that has been suggested is a thesaurus, or hierarchical classification of words. A model for semantic relations and a practical method for applying it are among the most important unsolved questions in the field of machine translation.

5.2. Computer-Program Refinement

The general nature of the computer program is sketched in the previous section (Machine Translation). It consists of routines for determination of Russian sentence structure and construction of English sentences with equivalent structure. In early cycles, these tasks are performed by the posteditor; the purpose of analysis is to relate the actions of the posteditor to the observable characteristics of the Russian sentences, so that the computer can be programmed to take similar actions under similar circumstances.

Sentence structure is symbolized, in Russian and in English, by the following observable characteristics: word order, particles, inflections, agreements, and punctuation. For automatic computation, these characteristics are represented by word number, sequence number, grammar code, and punctuation code. Analysis consists of correlation of these characteristics of the Russian sentence with the English structural codes or structural-connection codes inserted by the posteditor.

The technique is to bring together all occurrences of forms with a given grammar code—for example, all nouns in the dative plural. The analyst first tests whether any English structural code applies to all occurrences. For example, the English equivalents of Russian plural nouns must be inflected into the plural. A routine is established for English plural inflection, initiated when the Russian grammar code indicates a plural noun. Such grammatically determined routines are important, but they are few in number.

The next stage of analysis uses context of occurrence; all occurrences with a given grammar code are collected, and sorted according to grammar codes of contiguous forms. Taking the traditional rules of syntax as a guide, the analyst relates the English structural code to features of the context. The insertion of a preposition before the English equivalent of a Russian dative noun is thus related to the grammar codes of preceding occurrences. If the immediately preceding occurrence in Russian is a preposition, no additional preposition is required in English. Gradually extending the analysis over a wider context, the analyst connects dative plural nouns with preceding adjectives, preceding participial phrases, and prepositions preceding these modifiers. Syntactically determined computer routines for making the connections are written. The analyst is able to conclude that a dative noun, not connected with a preceding preposition, must be preceded by "to" in English translation.

There are two limitations on this type of analysis. First, the structure of the sentence may be ambiguous; an adjective may be placed between two nouns with which it agrees—in Russian, it might modify either of them. It seems probable that true structural ambiguity is rare and that in most cases a sufficiently complex routine can resolve apparent ambiguities. The second limitation is that the routines are complicated by rules that are necessary for the resolution of extremely rare constructions. Since the routines must be stored in a computer of limited size, it is not practical to seek "perfect" machine translation.

The analytic method described above is partially automatic; collection of occurrences with a given Russian grammar code, a given context, and a given English structural code is carried out by machine. With the explicit marking of structural connections planned for the second cycle, still more of the research operation becomes automatic, since it will be possible automatically to collect, for example, all dative plural nouns depending on prepositions, and to list all constructions that intervene between the preposition and the noun.

6. Conclusion

The RAND methodology is a system for preparing Russian scientific text on punched cards, for producing translations in analyzable form, and for exposing the relationships between the original and translated versions, semiautomatically, in such a way that translation can be programmed.

The research methodology described is, of course, designed to achieve satisfactory machine translation; the intermediate products are:

1. A descriptive grammar of the Russian language, as it is used today in scientific writing.

2. A working glossary of scientific Russian with the English equivalents required for accurate translation.

Solutions to both conceptual and technical problems of computer application in linguistic research are given in the other papers of this series.

10 On the Mechanization of Syntactic Analysis

Sydney M. Lamb

Any language has as part of its structure patterns according to which items are arranged on each of its strata. The term *tactics* is widely used for the analysis and description of arrangements, and the term *syntax* is traditionally used with reference to arrangements on the morphemic stratum. It is in connection with that stratum that the study of tactics has been of greatest interest in linguistics.

The items with which syntax is concerned can be of varying kinds, depending upon the school of thought. Some linguists regard the word as the basic unit of syntax; others make no syntax-morphology distinction, and we could apply the term *syntax* here also, with the morpheme as the basic unit. It is also possible to use items which tend to be smaller than words but larger than morphemes, and one unit of this kind is in fact what I prefer. I call it the *lexeme*.[1] But for purposes of this paper, let us think of syntax as being quite general with regard to the choice of the basic unit. The technique of analysis to be discussed applies for any of these kinds of items. After all, if one goes to the trouble of writing a computer program for syntactic analysis, one ought to make it as widely applicable as possible to the needs of different linguists. Indeed, the system as described in this paper, and the accompanying computer program, could also apply to the study of arrangements of phonemes or letters or syllables or morphographemes and perhaps also various nonlanguage phenomena which tend to occur in patterned linear arrangements. In other words, it is really a system for tactic analysis in general.

At any rate, whatever unit is taken as the basis of the tactic description

Note: Research performed at the University of California, Berkeley. Reprinted from *1961 International Conference on Machine Translation of Languages and Applied Language Analysis* (National Physical Laboratory Symposium No. 13), Vol. II, pp. 673–684, with the permission of the Controller of Her Britannic Majesty's Stationery Office, publisher, and of the author. The paper is somewhat abridged; more recent accounts of the author's theoretical position have superseded that originally included.

(word, lexeme, morpheme, or what-not) will be referred to as an *item* for purposes of this exposition.

The syntax may be completely described by a list of distribution classes of items, with the membership of each, and a list of constructions. A construction is characterized by specification of (1) the distribution classes which enter into it and their relative order, (2) the distribution-class membership of the constitutes. Lists of distribution classes of composite forms need not be given in the description (even though they exist), since they are defined by the constructions.

To say that a syntactic description consists of lists of distribution classes and constructions, however, is to specify only its form. There are any number of possible descriptions for a given language which could take this form, but only a few of them are good and only one is the best. It must further be specified, then, what constitutes the best solution. Alternatively, one could specify a procedure which, if followed, leads to the best solution. This latter approach has been popular in linguistic methodology, but it tends to be unnecessarily complicated. In syntax (or tactics in general) we can provide for good analysis and description very easily, by means of a simple definition. Taking for granted that the fundamental requirements of completeness, accuracy, and consistency are met, the best description of the syntax of a language is (naturally) the simplest. Simplicity in this area can be very clearly defined. *The simplest syntactic description is that which makes use of the smallest number of constructions.* It must also be specified that if two solutions have the same number of constructions, the one with simpler constructions is to be preferred. Thus we must now define *simple* with regard to constructions. A construction without discontinuous constituents is simpler than one with such constituents. And among constructions with different numbers of constituents, the simplest is that with the fewest constituents.

Having this simple definition of the best of all possible syntactic descriptions of a language, the analyst can use it either to show that a proposed solution is better than some alternative or, ideally, that it is better than all possible alternatives.

All valid criteria for determining immediate constituents can be deduced from the basic definitions. And most of the criteria which have been put forth by various linguists in recent years are valid in this sense. On the other hand, two principles are worthy of note as having been mentioned at one time or another without being valid. One of these is that constructions should always be binary or that they should always be binary except in the case of coordinate constructions having more than two members. The other, applicable only if items smaller than words, such as lexemes, are taken as the basis of the description, is that words must always be constituents.

Any procedure which arrives at a description satisfying the basic requirements is a valid one. If, therefore, one were expounding on syntactic analysis for the sake of human beings, any remarks added to the above having to do with procedures would serve only pedagogical purposes. On the other hand, if one wants to have a computer do syntactic analysis, it is necessary to specify a procedure in complete detail, since present-day machines are altogether lacking in intuition and ingenuity.

Let us now go into some general considerations relating to the application of computers to syntax, after which I will describe part of a specific procedure which I am currently working on.

The machine should use texts as its primary source of information, but it could also be enabled to ask for further information from the informant, just as human linguists do, in order to compensate for the absence of an infinite text. However, the machine will not be quite as dependent upon the informant as humans are, because, taking advantage of its capacity to process data at very high speeds, it will be able to work with much larger amounts of text than would be feasible for the human analyst. By the same token it should be able to do a more detailed analysis than is generally possible.

It need not be required in the initial attempts that the machine program be able to do the entire job of syntactic analysis. Provision can be made for it to admit failure on difficult problems, printing out the relevant data and leaving the solution up to human intelligence. Also, one can keep the initial stages simple by operating only in terms of binary constructions with continuous, obligatory constituents. Consideration of the more complicated types of constructions can be taken up at a later stage of the process.

The program should be designed to do its preliminary analysis on a fairly small portion of text (say around 5,000 items) at first, after which a larger amount can be considered for purposes of more detailed analysis. When the larger portion is brought in, its items can first be classified to the extent possible on the basis of the preliminary analysis, and tentative groupings based on the provisional constructions can be made. The data of the larger portion of text will thus be greatly simplified for the sake of the further analysis, even though some of the provisional conclusions may have to be rescinded.

For the remainder of this brief paper, let us consider just the preliminary analysis that is to be done on the first 5000-item portion of text.

In the course of the analysis, groupings of two kinds will be made. These may be referred to as *horizontal* and *vertical* groupings, or H-groups and V-groups for short. A *vertical grouping* or V-group is a grouping of items (and/or sequences of items) into a distribution class or an approximation to a distribution class. An H-group or *horizontal grouping* is a grouping of constituents of a construction (or tentative construction) into a constitute. Thus a combined horizontal and vertical grouping yields an actual or provisional constitute class. After an H-group or V-group has been made, it can be treated as a unit for the further conduct of the analysis. The term *unit* will be used from here on to refer to any item, V-group, or H-group.

But how is the machine going to make these V-groups and H-groups? Zellig Harris, in his procedure-oriented *Methods in Structural Linguistics*2, set up distribution classes of morphemes before considering horizontal groupings. To do so in a meaningful way requires that items grouped together be found in identical environments extending several items on either side. It would be futile to attempt such an approach even with a machine because a corpus of truly colossal proportions would be required, and even the computer has limits with regard to the volume of data that can be processed at high speed. One must design the procedure, then, so that the sharing of certain *significant* distributional properties, rather than certain total environments, will be the criterion for combining units into the same V-group. And such an approach requires that a certain amount of horizontal grouping be done first, since it is only in terms of H-groups that we can define significant distributional properties in advance of the completion of the analysis. Now it happens that there is a means of setting up H-groups which are at least usable approximations to constitutes of actual constructions, without the aid of any prior vertical grouping. This method makes use of a concept which I call the *token neighbor ratio,* or T/N ratio for short.

Any specific occurrence of an item may be called a *token* of it. The number of tokens of an item in a text is thus equal to the number of times that item occurs. Any item which occurs adjacent to another item is a *neighbor* of the latter. If two items A and B occur contiguous to each other, A at the left, then A may be called a *left neighbor* (LN) of B, and B may be called a *right neighbor* (RN) of A. The number of tokens of a given item in a text divided by the number of different right neighbors (i.e., RN types) may be called the *token/right-neighbor* (T/RN) *ratio* for that item in that text. Similarly, the ratio of the number of tokens to the number of different left neighbors (i.e., LN types) is the *token/left-neighbor* (T/LN) *ratio* for that item in that text. T/RN and T/LN are the two kinds of token/neighbor (T/N) ratios.

The first step in the analysis is to compute the two T/N ratios for every different item in the text. For a 5,000-item text, this takes about eight to ten minutes on an IBM 704, depending on the number of item types present. In the course of calculating these ratios for each item, lists of right and left neighbors will be formed but they will not be saved since the aggregate of such lists would soon become very bulky and those individual neighbor lists that will be needed later can be constructed again very rapidly when needed.

The highest T/N ratios identify the points of maximum restriction on freedom of combination, insofar as such identification can be made without prior information about the structure of the language.

The process continues with consideration of the item having the largest T/N ratio. This item we may call the *current most restricted unit,* or CMRU. Later the next largest ratio will be considered, and so forth, but various ratios will also be undergoing modification to give effect to horizontal and vertical groupings treated as units, so the second highest may not turn out to be the highest after the first has been dealt with.

Table 1 shows an ordered list of the items ("quasi-lexemes" in this case) having the highest T/N ratios in a particular English text, a selection from the writings of Sir Winston Churchill.3

The neighbor class with respect to which the CMRU has the highest ratio may be called the SNC, for *small neighbor class.* It is necessarily small. Moreover, its smallness has significance since the item of which its members are neighbors occurs with relatively high frequency in the text. That is, the

Table 1. Highest T/N Ratios of Items (Quasi-Lexemes) in a 5,000-Item English Text, Excluding Ratios of Punctuation Lexemes

Item	Token Count	LN Count	RN Count	T/N
are	82		6	13.67
-s (verbal third singular)	53	4		13.25
-'s	85	9		9.44
new	8	1		8.00
have	58		8	7.25
own	6	1		6.00
Adolf	5		1	5.00
the	327	66		4.95
but	9	2		4.50
they	40		9	4.44
seem	4		1	4.00
call	4		1	4.00
Rhineland	4	1		4.00
he	75		21	3.55
be	28	8		3.50
Reichswehr	7	2		3.50
-pl (nominal plural)	223		67	3.33
German	34	11		3.09
force	9		3	3.00
it	24		8	3.00

highest T/N ratio can be the highest only by virtue of the fact that the size of T (number of tokens) is relatively large while the size of N (number of neighbors) is relatively small. It does not necessarily follow, however, that this item (the CMRU) and these neighbors are partners of each other in a construction nor that this small neighbor class constitutes a distribution class.

In designing the procedure, one is faced with alternatives at this point. One could consider the SNC to be a first approximation to a distribution class. In this case, if it has more than one member, it would be necessary to look for the presence of certain relationships of its members to each other. Specifically, it would be necessary to find out whether any of its members can have any members of this same class as neighbors. For all those members which can, separate position classes (left to right) would have to be set up, and it is even possible (though not likely for the first neighbor class studied because of its small size) that more than one set of such classes would be present.

A simpler alternative is to let the machine refrain from making any vertical groupings at this point, waiting until more information is available as a result of the formation of additional H-groups. In general, we will want to combine units into a vertical grouping *only when they are found to share the same partner in H-groups which, in turn, also share the same partner in horizontal groupings of the next higher degree.* For example, if A, B, C, . . . are items, and if AB and AC are H-groups, then that fact alone is not sufficient grounds for grouping B and C together (*cf., John left* and *John Smith*). But if AB-D and AC-D (or D-AB and D-AC) also become H-groups, then B and C will be combined in a V-group. Even the grouping under these circumstances could be incorrect, however, so re-examination of V-groups will be necessary after further analysis has been done.

As soon as the CMRU is obtained, then, it will be combined with each member of the SNC into one or more H-groups.4 But since such groupings will often be incorrect, there must be provision for re-appraising H-groups at suitable later points, revising as necessary. Let us take an example. As we might expect, frequently occurring prepositions in English have relatively high T/RN ratios. Suppose that the preposition *in* in a text occurs several times, having as different right neighbors *sand, water,* and *the.* The H-groups *in sand, in water,* and *in the* will be formed. Obviously it is necessary that the last of these be rescinded sooner or later. And it will be, as soon as certain V-groups are made. The article *the* has been combined with the preceding *in* simply because the machine does not yet know that the nouns following it belong together in a V-group. (Let us leave adjectives out of the picture, to keep our example simple.) But as the process continues, these nouns will gradually be grouped together, and the resulting V-groups will be treated as units. Then, if re-appraisal of affected H-groups is conducted as each new vertical grouping is made, it will eventually turn out that the T/RN ratio of *the* is higher than the ratio which led to the combining of *the* with *in,* and that incorrect H-group will at that point be dissolved.

It will be noted that although the procedure begins by considering immediate environments only, wider environments automatically come into consideration as horizontal groups are made.

A detailed summary of the first stage of the process follows:

Definitions

Item: ultimate constituent.

Unit: item, H-group, or V-group.

H-group: horizontal grouping; i.e., constitute of a construction or of an approximation to a construction.

V-group: vertical grouping; i.e., provisional distribution class.

CH-group: complex H-group; i.e., H-group in which at least one partner is itself an H-group.

CMRU: current most restricted unit; i.e., the unit currently having the highest T/N ratio.

NC: neighbor class; i.e., the set of units which are neighbors (right or left) of a given unit in a given text.

SNC: small neighbor class; i.e., the NC with respect to which the CMRU has the highest T/N ratio.

Main Routine

I. Perform A on every different item in the text.

II. Get the CMRU and for each member of the SNC as partner form a new H-group. For each new H-group, (1) record its membership in reference list; (2) replace it in the text (each occurrence) by a unit symbol for the group (reference list permits restoration in case of later revision); (3) if it is a CH-group, go to B, specifying which partner is complex (if both are complex go to B twice). Perform A for each new H-group and for all units affected by the new groupings (replacing previous information now obsolete), namely (1) units occurring as neighbors of the new H-groups and (2) those members of the SNC which still have occurrence apart from the new H-groups.

III. *Switch,* having the values *plus* and *minus.* (Starts as *minus,* can be set *plus* by B and is reset *minus* by *IV.*) If *minus* return to *II;* if *plus* go to *IV.*

IV. Reset switch *III* to *minus*. Form new V-group(s) as indicated by *B*. For each, (1) record its membership in reference list; (2) in text, replace tokens of members by symbol for the group. Perform *A* for each new V-group and for all other units affected by the new grouping. Re-appraise all affected H-groups, revising as needed; upon revision, reappraise any affected V-groups, revising as needed. Return to *II*.

Subroutines

A. Determine the T/N ratios of the specified unit.

B. Split the specified complex partner into its constituents and add the CH-groups (in this form) to the list of CH-groups; let the other partner be called Other Partner. If Other Partner and either constituent of the complex partner match the two members of corresponding position of any other CH-group in the list, set the switch (*III*) *plus;* the third (nonmatching) constituents are to be combined as a V-group.

At the time of writing, the process is operational on the computer only up to the point at which proper justification is found for making the first vertical grouping. In performing the analysis on some newspaper text from the Associated Press which had kindly been furnished by the MT group at the Massachusetts Institute of Technology, the machine reached that point after forming 31 H-groups, three of which were complex. In this text, capitalization of the following letter was everywhere segmented as a separate item by the M.I.T. group, so much of the horizontal grouping involved combining proper names (such as Poland, Gomulka, and Egypt) with their preceding capitalization. The first vertical grouping consisted of *united* and *mrs*. Both had been combined with preceding capitalization, and each of the two resulting H-groups was found to have capitalization as its only right neighbor.[5]

This is, of course, only a beginning. But it is the beginning of a system which may eventually be able to reduce the time required for analyzing the structure of a language from several years down to a few months or even weeks.

<h2 style="text-align:center">References</h2>

1. Even though it is defined somewhat differently from the lexeme of Bernard Bloch and Charles F. Hockett; *cf.*, Hockett's *A Course in Modern Linguistics* New York (1958), Chapter 19.

2. University of Chicago Press, Chicago (1951).

3. This text consists of the first 5,000 quasi-lexemes in the first chapter of the *Life Magazine* edition of *The Second World War*, New York, (1959). Quasi-lexemes, for this text, are the items arrived at by segmenting (1) at spaces, (2) punctuation lexemes (including capitalization at the beginnings of sentences only), (3) certain nominal (-pl, -'s) and verbal

(-s, -ed, -en, -ing) suffixes, and (4) -n't and -'ll; where such segmented forms are written so that their morphemic identity in different environments is preserved, regardless of variation which might be present in a graphemic representation.

4. The procedure has been revised so that the CMRU is combined only with that member of the SNC which occurs most frequently as neighbor of the CMRU.

5. When the revised procedure (cf. preceding note) was used on the Winston Churchill text on which Tables 1 is based, the first vertical grouping formed consisted of *he* and *they*.

11 Keyword-in-Context Index for Technical Literature (KWIC Index)

H. P. Luhn

1. Introduction

Specialized indexes to technical literature are an established means for directing engineers and scientists to sources of information pertinent to their current interest. Whatever the specific purpose of an index may be, a substantial amount of intellectual effort is required to compile it. In many cases, the time presently required for compiling and updating an index interferes seriously with its usefulness at the instant of publication. This is particularly true of bibliographical indexes to material currently being published in such media as technical journals, magazines or technical governmental, institutional and private industry reports.

The accelerated pace of scientific developments in recent years has accentuated the perishable nature of new information. As a result there is a pressing demand for speedier communication in this area. It appears doubtful that this demand can be satisfied without breaking with some of the standards conventionally applied to the compilation of literature indexes.

In what follows the relationship between user and index is examined, and it is shown that for new information, which as it appears is only a fraction of the total information accumulated in an area, relatively rough clues can answer the user's needs. It is then argued that such clues can be generated entirely by machine in the form of a series of extractions each containing a significant, or key, word as its nucleus. Samples of indexes compiled entirely by machine methods are presented in support of this argument.

Note: This work was performed in the Advanced Systems Development Division, International Business Machines Corporation, Yorktown Heights, New York. Originally released as ASDD Report RC-127, August 31, 1959, and delivered before the Division of Chemical Literature at the 136th Meeting of the American Chemical Society, this paper is reprinted with the permission of IBM: a section on "A Derived Code for the Identification of Bibliographical Items" is omitted here.

2. Dissemination v. Retrieval

In the area of communication served by technical literature, the two main functions being performed are the dissemination of information on the one side and the retrieval of information on the other. A publication, when issued, serves to broadcast new information. After the publication has fulfilled this purpose and has been retired to the Library and properly stored, it serves as a potential reference in the process of information retrieval. In the first case its news aspect is predominant, while in the second its historical aspect is predominant.

It is here argued that by means of a rather few clues an expert can judge whether an article touches upon his field of interest and adjust himself momentarily to whatever new information may be furnished. In the case of information retrieval the same expert expects that the information furnished be adjusted to him, that is, to his rather specific interest at the moment.

Because of the difference in attitude in these two cases it is here proposed to consider two types of indexes, namely a dissemination index and a retrieval index, each serving its respective functions and being different as to scope and form. In accordance with this concept a dissemination index would be an instrument prepared with minimum effort and disseminated in the shortest possible time. As such it would fulfill the important task of prompt notification, and its usefulness would be substantially of temporary character. For this reason its publication by inexpensive printing methods would appear justifiable and adequate. A retrieval index, on the other hand, would be an instrument prepared with care in due course, incorporating all those features which will enhance its usefulness as a permanent tool of reference. Most likely it would take the form of a cumulative index and would obsolete dissemination indexes previously issued for material covered by it.

3. Indexing by Means of Keywords in Context

The usefulness of an index depends on the manner in which index entries have been organized. The establishment of categories by subject or other appropriate characteristics is the conventional means by which such organization is accomplished. The establishment of categories and the assignment to such categories of index entries is a matter of judgment and experience and constitutes a considerable part of the intellectual effort involved in the manual compilation of indexes. Various indexers will usually differ in their approaches to this task and will also differ in their interpretation of the material to be indexed. While there may be differences of opinion as to the effectiveness of this or that scheme, the important fact seems to be that any reasonable scheme of ordering, if understood, will save time in locating desired information.

In striving for a speedy method of organizing an index, the question arises as to which of various possible schemes is adaptable to fully automatic processing. Clearly, some means of ordering is required that is based on criteria extracted from the text itself rather than assigned in accordance with human judgment.

The simplest format of a quickly assembled index might be an alphabetic listing of keywords, very much as in the index to a book. The simplicity of such an index is, however, predicated on the fact that the reader has been introduced to the subject matter treated by the book. In dealing with a variety of subjects, as would be the case in the problem under discussion, the significance of such single keywords could, in most instances, be determined only by referring to the statement from which the keyword had been chosen. This somewhat tedious procedure may be alleviated to a significant degree by listing selected keywords together with surrounding words that act as modifiers pointing up the more specific sense in which a keyword has been applied. This method of indexing words is well established in the process of compiling concordances of important works of literature of the past. The added degree of information conveyed by such keyword-in-context indexes, or "KWIC Indexes" for short, can readily be provided by automatic processing.

Keyword-in-context indexing may be carried out on various levels, depending on the purpose an index is to serve. The process may be applied to the title of an article, its abstract or its entire text. Keywords need only be defined as those which characterize a subject more than others. To derive them, rules have to be established for differentiating between what is significant and nonsignificant. Since significance is difficult to predict, it is more practical to isolate it by rejecting all obviously non-significant or "common" words, with the risk of admitting certain words of questionable status. Such words may subsequently be eliminated or tolerated as so much "noise." A list of nonsignificant words would include articles, conjunctions, prepositions, auxiliary verbs, certain adjectives and words such as "report," "analysis," "theory," and the like. It would become the task of an editor to extend this list as required. The remaining significant or "key" words would be extracted from the text together with a certain number of words that precede and follow them. By making the keywords assume a fixed position within the extracted portions and by arranging these portions in alphabetic order of the keywords, the KWIC Index is generated.

The format of a KWIC Index is illustrated in Fig. 1. The initial letters of the alphabetized keywords form a column which guides the eye when scanning for desired words. The number to the right of each line identifies the corresponding document. The sample shown in Fig. 1 was derived from

Keyword-in-Context Bibliographical Index

```
                              EXCITATION OF PROTONS IN HELIUM II B      0011
     OF ATOMIC AND MOLECULAR   EXCITATION BY A TRAPPED-ELECTRON ME      0150
                     THERMAL   EXCITATIONS IN LIQUID HE3.               1465
       ENERGIES OF GROUND AND  EXCITED NUCLEAR CONFIGURATIONS IN TH     0452
                              EXCITED STATES OF V51 AND CR53.           1691
                      4-PLUS   EXCITED STATE IN. OSMIUM-188.            1717
    NTERNAL PHOTOEFFECT AND    EXCITON DIFFUSION IN CADMIUM AND ZIN     0123
      OF THE CONTRIBUTION OF   EXCITONS TO THE COMPLEX DIELECTRIC       1555
                     THERMAL   EXPANSION OF SOME CRYSTALS WITH THE      0136
             ENERGY LEVELS IN  F18 FROM THE N14/ALPHA,ALPHA/N14 AND     0547
     ON FROM AL27-PLUS-P AND   F19-PLUS-P.                              0239
    TIC MEASUREMENTS OF THE    FE-CR SPINELS.                           1603
                     BARIUM    FERRATE III.                             0326
       MAGNETOSTATIC MODES IN  FERRIMAGNETIC SPHERES.                   0059
              NICKEL-IRON      FERRITE.                                 0397
          TRANSITION TO THE    FERROELECTRIC STATE IN BARIUM TITANA     0413
     SUPERCONDUCTIVITY AND     FERROMAGNETISM IN ISOMORPHOUS COMPOU     0089
    INTERPLANETARY MAGNETIC    FIELD AND ITS CONTROL OF COSMIC-RAY      0589
              .MAGNETIC        FIELD DEPENDENCE OF ULTRASONIC ATTEN     0080
             RELATIVISTIC      FIELD THEORY OF UNSTABLE PARTICLES.      0283
                    QUANTUM    FIELD THEORIES WITH COMPOSITE PARTIC     0669
      A GENERALLY CONVARIANT   FIELD THEORY.                            1826
     AND SURFACE STATES FROM   FIELD-INDUCED CHANGES IN SURFACE REC     0369
       NGULAR DISTRIBUTIONS IN FISSION INDUCED BY ALPHA PARTICLES.      0536
       UTRON CROSS SECTIONS OF FISSIONABLE NUCLEI.                      0203
    AL COSMIC-RAY INTENSITY    FLUCTUATIONS OBSERVED AT SOUTHERN ST     1798
                              FLUX OF COSMIC-RAY PARTICLES WITH Z-      0597
       NEUTRINO CORRELATION IN FORBIDDEN BETA DECAY.                    0244
                              FOURIER COEFFICIENTS OF CRYSTAL POTE      0073
       RVATION IN THE DECAY OF FREE AND BOUND LAMBDA PARTICLES.         0605
              STEADY-STATE     FREE PRECESSION IN NUCLEAR MAGNETIC      1693
                              FREQUENCY SHIFT OF THE ZERO-FIELD HY      0449
                  DECAY OF     GADOLINIUM-159.                          0262
                              GAMMA RADIATION FROM AL27-PLUS-P AND      0239
      ECTIONAL CORRELATION OF  GAMMA RAYS IN GE72.                      0229
      CISION DETERMINATION OF  GAMMA RAYS FOLLOWING. P,P-PRIME-GAMMA    0532
                              GAMMA-RAY THRESHOLD METHOD AND THE O      0461
     P/S32 AND S32/P,P-PRIME   GAMMA/S32.                               1702
     ONSTANT OF YTTRIUM IRON   GARNET AT O DEG K.                       0395
                 LORENTZIAN    GAS AND HOT ELECTRONS.                   1567
       TIBILITY OF AN ELECTRON GAS AT HIGH DENSITY.                     0328
       UCTIVITY OF AN ELECTRON GAS IN A GASEOUS PLASMA.                 0001
       OF AN ELECTRON GAS IN A GASEOUS PLASMA.                          0001
       DUCED BY VARIOUS BUFFER GASES.                                   0449
                     BUFFER    GASES.                                   0450
                    IONIZED    GAS.                                     1441
     EZORESISTANCE IN N-TYPE   GA,AS.                                   1533
       IN ELECTRON-IRRADIATED  GE AT 80 DEG K.                          0362
     LATION OF GAMMA RAYS IN   GE72.                                    0229
     NERAL RELATIVITY AS THE   GENERATORS OF COORDINATE TRANSFORMAT     0287
     ETORESISTANCE IN N-TYPE   GERMANIUM AT LOW TEMPERATURES.           0317
       CONDUCTION ELECTRONS IN GERMANIUM.                               0298
       IATIVE RECOMBINATION IN GERMANIUM.                               0330.
       PARTICLES IN LINEARIZED GRAVITATIONAL THEORY.                    0674
```

Fig. 1

titles of technical papers. Since a title may contain several keywords there would be index entries in as many places as there are keywords. For instance, on the sample page the concept "Gamma Rays in Ge 72," will be found under "Gamma" and under "Ge."

A maximum of sixty characters of a title are printed to serve as the index entry. This provides for an adequate number of letters on either side of the centrally located keyword for including immediately associated significant words. The process of slicing a fixed number of letters out of a title necessitates mutilations of some words on either end of the resulting fragment.

4. Organization of a Bibliographical KWIC Index

As is evident from the preceding explanation, the grouping of a given set of bibliographical items into subject categories is eliminated and is replaced by a grouping according to keywords. This arrangement overcomes all arguments as to the appropriateness of assignment of certain items to pre-established subject headings and abolishes the nondescript category of "Miscellaneous." If the index is based on titles of documents, its quality depends on how well the authors have composed the titles of their papers. It will be a matter of experience as to whether KWIC indexing needs to be extended to include abstracts or even portions of the text in order to provide the degree of resolution required under given circumstances.

One of the problems a user of a KWIC Index faces is that of synonyms and variations in word usage and spelling. It must however be assumed that the expert in his field is sufficiently familiar with such variations and is resourceful enough to overcome this problem, as he had to in the past. It is of course quite simple to insert at appropriate places of the index a "see also" cross reference to take care of the less obvious instances. This convenience does not call for additional intellectual effort on the part of the editors once the need for such a reference has been established. Thereafter the insertion of such references will be provided automatically by the machine.

The type of bibliography here proposed would necessarily consist of two parts: a listing of the bibliographical items and the KWIC Index. The items would be listed in alphabetical order of the authors' names and comprise author, title and source data. This list would thus serve as an author index.

Since each KWIC Index entry must be related to the bibliographical items it stands for, there arises a problem of identification. A simple means of identification would be the use of consecutive reference numbers assigned to the bibliographical items in sequence as listed alphabetically by author. These numbers would be given after each index entry (see Fig. 1) and would refer the user to the corresponding item in the bibliography. Such reference numbers are limited to the function just mentioned and would serve no useful purpose outside of the individual bibliography to which they have been applied.

One of the principal advantages resulting from the type indexes here proposed is the promptness, owing to their machine origin, with which they can be disseminated. It would therefore become feasible to issue KWIC Indexes at frequent intervals, perhaps monthly. While this would fulfill the demand for currency, the subscriber of such a service would, however, soon be inconvenienced by having to handle a multiplicity of individual issues. To facilitate bibliographical search of material from the time it is published until it is noted in some more refined reference manual, it would be most useful if the KWIC Indexes were furnished in cumulative form over certain periods. Since they are to be produced automatically, the effort and cost for providing this extra convenience is quite moderate.

5. Automatic Preparation of KWIC Indexes

The various steps involved in the automatic preparation of KWIC Indexes for technical literature will be described briefly and without tying them to any particular type of information processing equipment, except by way of example.

5.1. Creation of Machine-Readable Record

Automatic processing requires that information be available in machine-readable form. Although print-reading devices might eventually translate printed characters into machinable codes, there are today many instances of machine-readable records being produced as a by-product of typing and typesetting operations. These are available in the form of punched tapes or cards and can readily serve as input to present information processing equipment.

In the case of technical literature, the typesetting of many professional journals and of technical magazines is done on punched-tape controlled Monotype or Teletypesetter equipment. Flexowriters are often used for preparing technical reports in order to produce a punched tape for various subsequent retyping operations. In these instances no further manual operations are required to obtain the input for automatic processing.

Where no such records are available, they must be prepared by hand. A most convenient method entails the preparation of punched cards by manual key-punching from the printed text of the portions needed for the process. These portions are the author, title and source of a document if the KWIC Index is to be derived from titles only. Otherwise the abstract or even the text would have to be hand-punched.

Limiting the description to the use of titles only, the punching of cards would best be performed in accordance with certain rules which will facilitate machine processing not only for the creation of the KWIC Index but the creation of many other useful records for facilitating various tasks of publishers, information centers, documentalists, and librarians.

These rules would standardize the format of cards and the manner in which information is to be recorded. For instance, it might be advantageous to prepare a separate card for each author and one or several cards each for the title and the source. The arrangement would be such that a listing of these cards by automatic printing devices would produce a bibliography of good appearance. Furthermore the standardization of these card records will simplify the programming of information processing equipment for performing the routines necessary for deriving identification codes and for extracting the index entries. As was mentioned before, the selection of keywords might best be carried out by rejecting insignificant words of the kind previously described. A dictionary of such words must therefore be compiled and revised in machine-readable form so that it may be transferred to the memory of the machine for reference during processing.

5.2. Machine Processing

There is no intention here to go into the details of programming information-processing equipment, particularly since many different types of machines may be used to obtain similar effects. Basically, the following major functions need to be performed on each record fed into the machine.

First an identification code is derived. Each word of the title is then looked up in the dictionary of insignificant words stored in the machine. For each word not contained in the dictionary an index entry is generated by shifting the text of the title so that the word in question will start at position twenty-five of a sixty-position field. The contents of this field is then stored together with the identifying code.

After this process has been repeated for each of the documents which are to constitute the bibliography, the records are sorted in the alphabetic order of their identification code and are printed out in the form shown in Fig. 2. The index entries are then sorted in the alphabetic order of the keywords and are printed out in a form similar to that shown in Fig. 3 with their identification codes at the right. Figs. 2 and 3* are typical pages of an index.

---

* From *Bibliography and Auto-Index, Literature on Information Retrieval and Machine Translation,* Service Bureau Corporation, New York. (Second Edition, June 1959; First Edition, September 1958).

Bibliography

```
ADAIWC-55-CIS  ADAIR WC
               CITATION INDEXES FOR SCIENTIFIC LITERATURES.
               AMERICAN DOCUMENTATION, 6, /1/, 1955.
ADAMS -56-INR  ADAMS S
               INFORMATION - A NATIONAL RESOURCE.
               AMER DOC V. VII NO. 2 APR 1956
ADIAWC-55-CIS  ADIAR WC
               CITATION INDEXES FOR SCIENCE.
               AM. DOCUMENT. 6, 31 /1955/.
ADKIBW- -DPL   ADKINSON BW
               DATA PROCESSING AND LIBRARY OPERATIONAL PROBLEMS.
               LIBRARY OF CONGRESS
ADKIBW-56-IUR  ADKINSON BW LIBRARY OF CONGRESS
               INTERNATIONAL UTILIZATION OF RECORDED KNOWLEDGE.
               CHAPT. VIII IN DOCUMENTATION IN ACTION REINHOLD PUB CORP
               1956.
AEC RC-53-ECS  AEC REPORT CRO 102, UNIVERSITY OF TENNESSE NOVEMBER 1953.
               EDGE-PUNCHED CARDS FOR SCIENTIFIC LITERATURE REFERENCES.
               AEC REPORT CRO 102, UNIVERSITY OF TENNESSEE NOVEMBER 1953.
AHLIJT-56-GUF  AHLIN JT
               GENERAL USE OF FOUR-HOLE RANDOMLY PUNCHED CARDS IN FILE
               SEARCHING APPLICATIONS.
               PAM 1702 DEC. 1956 RESEARCH LIB. SAN JOSE CAL.
ALEXSM-57-DPI  ALEXANDER SM
               STEVENS ME
               DATA PROCESSORS FOR INFORMATION RETRIEVAL PURPOSES.
               PAPER PRESENTED AT THE 132TH MEETING OF THE AMER. CHEM.
               SOCIETY. NEW YORK, SEPT. 10, 1957
ALLEEP-43-PCN  ALLEN EP
               A PUNCHED CARD FOR NEOPLASTIC DISEASES.
               NEW ZEALAND MED J. 42 121 1943
ALLOAJ- -IRM   ALLOT AJ
               INFORMATION RETRIEVAL METHODS USED BY THE U S ARMY ORDNANCE
               CORP IN DEPOT OPERATIONS.
               DEPT. OF THE ARMY
AMDOC -53-CRM  ABSTRACT IN AM. DOC. APR. 1953.
               CORRESPONDENCE REGARDING METALLURGICAL DOCUMENTATION OF THE.
               CORDONNIER-BATTEN SYSTEM OF PUNCHED CARDS.
               ABSTRACT IN AM. DOC. APR. 1953.
AMDOC -53-FSE  ABSTRACT IN AM. DOC. JANUARY 1953.
               FILMOREX SYSTEM FOR ELECTRONIC SELECTION OF MICROFILM CARDS.
               ABSTRACT IN AM. DOC. JANUARY 1953.
AMERDI-56-RCR  AMER DOCUMENTATION INST. 1956-1957 1957 16 PP.
               ROSTER OF CURRENT RESEARCH IN DOCUMENTATION AND
               LIBRARIANSHIP.
               AMER DOCUMENTATION INST. 1956-1957 1957 16 PP.
AMERDO-52-GCR  AMER. DOC. III 1952 91-94
               THE GENESIS AND CHARACTERISTICS OF REPORT LITERATURE.
               AMER. DOC. III 1952 91-94
```

Fig. 2

The finished prints of the bibliography and the index are mounted in two columns of 125 lines each for photographic reduction to fit $8\frac{1}{2} \times 11$ size pages. The whole material is then printed and bound, and the KWIC Index is ready for mailing.

6. Conclusion

So far only a few KWIC Index services have been installed on an experimental basis. While user-acceptance has been very favorable, only experience will tell to what extent the objectives of this new device can be realized.

The following advantages are apparent at this time:

Key Words-In-Context Index

```
                    LIST OF   ABBREVIATED AND FULL TITLES OF TECHN    INSTSI-57-LAF
ENT AND PROOF SERVICES,       ABERDEEN PROVING GROUND.               PERRJW-57-NIS
URING COUNTRY, MACHINES       ABOARD UNEARTH INFORMATION BURIED IN   BENSLC-55-DCI
   CARDS TO SORT INFRARED     ABSORPTION AND CHEMICAL STRUCTURE.DA   KUENL -51-NCH
CARDS INDEXING INFRARED       ABSORPTION SPECTROGRAMS.               KEUNLE-52-CIW
GRAPHIC SCHEME BASED ON       ABSTRACT AND INDEX CARDS.              BISHC - -BSB
TIC INFORMATION.* USING       ABSTRACT AND INDEX PUBLICATIONS.       SEWEW -57-RTI
                              ABSTRACT ARCHIVE OF ALCOHOL LITERATU   JELLEM-48-AAA
        PUBLISHING MODERN     ABSTRACT BULLETINS.                    WEILBH- -PMA
COMPANY PHARMACEUTICAL        ABSTRACT BULLETIN.                     SEWEW -54-PIC
        A PUNCHED CARD        ABSTRACT FILE ON SOLID STATE AND TRA   PATTLD-55-PCA
                    THE       ABSTRACT OF THE TECHNICAL REPORT.      CORTE -55-ATR
                              ABSTRACT THEORY OF RETRIEVAL CODING.   MALOCJ- -ATR
             RELATION OF AN   ABSTRACT TO ITS ORIGINAL.              DYSOG -51-RAI
FROM JOURNAL ARTICLE TO       ABSTRACT.                              BIOLAB-56-BRJ
ID SYSTEM OF CODING AND       ABSTRACTING CHEMICAL LITERATURE USIN   KIRSS -56-SRS
          SYMPOSIUM ON        ABSTRACTING AND INDEXING.              CHEMEN-52-SAI
THE ORGANIZATION OF AN        ABSTRACTING SERVICE.                   MCGEJH- -OAS
WABASH CUTS WAY BILL          ABSTRACTING EXPENSE.                   EASTWR-50-WCW
IL OF SCIENTIFIC UNIONS       ABSTRACTING BOARD.                     BOUTPR-56-ICS
                              ABSTRACTING AND INDEXING SERVICES IN   MILEJT-57-AIS
       AN EVALUATION OF       ABSTRACTING JOURNALS AND INDEXES.      SMITMH- -EAJ
SLANTING IN SCIENTIFIC        ABSTRACTING PUBLICATIONS.              HERNS - -SSS
TERNATIONAL COOPERATIVE       ABSTRACTING ON BUILDING.* AN APPRAIS   EVANAB- -ICA
ION AND COORDINATION IN       ABSTRACTING AND DOCUMENTATION.         FRANO -6 -CCA
              THE ICSU        ABSTRACTING BOARD.* THE STORY OF A V   BOUTGA- -IAB
Y OF CURRENT PERIODICAL       ABSTRACTING AND BIBLIOGRAPHIES.        BESTT -52-IBD
OVERAGE BY INDEXING AND       ABSTRACTING SERVICE.                   HIMWWA-54-SWM
                              ABSTRACTING BOARD OF INTERNATIONAL C   BOUTGA-56-ABI
             A RUSSIAN        ABSTRACTING SERVICE IN THE FIELD OF    BEYFE -56-RAS
DOMLY PUNCHED CARDS FOR       ABSTRACTING PUBLICATIONS AND REPORTS   SHERJ -53-UAH
                              ABSTRACTING AND LIBRARY WORK IN THE    NATURE-53-ALW
              TECHNICAL       ABSTRACTING AND CHEMICAL INDEXING IN   INSTSI- -TAC
CIENTIFIC AND TECHNICAL       ABSTRACTING AND INDEXING SERVICES.     CONFAS- -PCA
ION PROCESSING- SCIENCE       ABSTRACTING.                           HUTCE -56-CIP
.COOPERATION IN PHYSICS       ABSTRACTING.                           CROWBM- -ICP
              PHYSICS         ABSTRACTING.                           GRAYDE-50-PA
    AN EXPERIMENT IN AUTO     ABSTRACTING.                           IBM RC-58-EAA
L CONFERENCE ON SCIENCE       ABSTRACTING, 1949, FINAL REPORT.       UNESPA-49-ICS
D FOR THE BIBLIOGRAPHY,       ABSTRACTING, AND INDEXING OF CHEMICA   GULLC -46-PCM
IBLIOGRAPHIC, INDEXING,       ABSTRACTING, AND REVIEW MEDIA.         FLEMTP-58-RDK
VARIATION IN CONTENT OF       ABSTRACTS ACCORDING TO USE.            FLEIM -56-VCA
A SURVEY OF SCIENTIFIC        ABSTRACTS AND INDEXING SERVICES.       VAROWW-49-SSA
YPES OF CHEMICAL PATENT       ABSTRACTS FOR PUNCH CARD USE.          TAPIEW- .-CST
           BIOLOGICAL         ABSTRACTS IN AN ERA OF AUTOMATION.     GARFE - -BAE
                              ABSTRACTS OF DOCUMENTATION LITERATUR   BROWH -55-ADL
      A PUNCH CARD FOR        ABSTRACTS OF BACTERIOLOGICAL PAPERS.   READRW-53-PCA
REPARATION OF AUTOMATIC       ABSTRACTS ON THE 704 DATA PROCESSING   SAVATR-58-PAA
          THE CHEMICAL        ABSTRACTS SERVICE- GOOD BUY OR GOOD-   CRANEJ-55-CAS
```

Fig. 3

1. Because of the mechanical method of preparation, more information may be displayed than would have been practical by conventional means.
2. Keywords-in-context permit the cross correlation of subjects to an extent not realizable by conventional procedures.
3. KWIC indexes provide an invaluable basis for the compilation of reference material by professional catalogers and indexers.

It has to be kept in mind that machine products of the kind discussed here can never reach the level of perfection that humans are capable of and that there will always be residual effort left for humans. It is hoped that in the case of the KWIC Index this effort is acceptable to the user.

12 Automatic Phrase Matching

Gerard Salton

1. Introduction

In 1957, Luhn suggested a fully automatic procedure for the processing of written texts, based on the frequency of occurrence of words within the texts.[1] Specifically, use of high-frequency words was advocated for purposes of content identification, and document retrieval was to be effected by manipulation of the corresponding word frequency lists. The suggested procedure, while admittedly imperfect, is still used as a basis for many automatic text processing programs.

More recently, the original statistical methods have been modified in various ways: by using word stems rather than the original word forms to identify document content; by introducing synonym dictionaries to lessen the effects of vocabulary variations; and, most importantly, by identifying relations between certain words to be used as content identifiers in conjunction with the surrounding words.

As a result, many of the word matching systems are now being replaced by *phrase* processing systems, in which the basic units being manipulated are sets of normalized words together with specified relations between them.

In the present report, a variety of methods are described for the automatic generation and manipulation of phrases. The phrase matching procedures used in the SMART document retrieval system to match semantically similar but syntactically quite distinct structures are described in detail, as a specific example of present capabilities.

2. The Content Analysis Problem

In information processing, the structure of written data is of particular importance, because a large part of the information of interest is repre-

Note: This research was conducted in the Computation Laboratory of Harvard University and was sponsored in part by the National Science Foundation under grant GN-360. Reprinted from the preprints of the 1965 International Conference on Computational Linguistics by permission of the author and the Association for Machine Translation and Computational Linguistics.

sented by combinations of words in the natural language. If it is desired to use written data directly as part of an information system, it becomes necessary to define transformations designed to reduce the original input in the natural language into some predetermined standard form. In particular, it would be useful if a text were reducible automatically into a set of controlled terms complemented by a set of well-defined relational indicators.

Before determining the extent to which the known structure of the natural language can help in this endeavor, it may be well to list some of the difficulties which stand in the way of an automatic content analysis:

1. The synonym and homograph problem for individual text words (many words can be used to represent the same concept; some words can represent many different concepts).
2. The problem of semantically equivalent, but syntactically distinct, constructions (a large number of different constructions can be used in the natural language to express the same thought, for example, "the children broke the window," "the children used rocks to break the window," "rocks were thrown by the children, and as a result the window was broken," etc.).*
3. The problem of indirect reference, including the use of pronouns and other referents to describe information not specifically stated but presumed known from the context. (The dependent structures often straddle sentence boundaries in such cases, as in the example: "*Someone* opened the door. It was our *father*.")
4. The problem of existing relations which are unstated, but may nevertheless be deduced from relationships actually available (in the Syntol system, for example, "associative" relations between a first element and an action, and between the same action and a second element, automatically generate a "consecutive" relation between elements one and two).† 4, 5, 6
5. The grouping problem which arises because constructions may refer to a variable number of unspecified items, or to a set of items defined elsewhere, for example, "*all words starting with 'x'* are of foreign origin."

It is clear that any one of these difficulties would by itself be sufficient to prevent, in almost all cases, an analysis of written texts into simple components. The presence of homographs and synonyms effectively guarantees that the words used in a text will have to be properly standardized before being used, and the multiplicity of semantically equivalent structures indicates that the isolation of word groupings together with normalized relations between them is likely to be an operation of great difficulty.

The normalization of the vocabulary may be attempted by using a variety

---

* A large number of examples of this type are included in Refs. 2 and 3.

† A solution to this problem is sometimes sought in the construction of automatic deductive systems. 7, 8

of synonym dictionaries and thesauri. Word groupings and relations between words, on the other hand, must be determined in part by utilizing the known structure of the language. This problem is examined in more detail in the next few paragraphs.

3. Sentence Kernelization

It is well known that at least some of the structure of sentences in the natural language is based on syntax, and that this structure is revealed by syntactic analysis. A variety of programs exist to perform automatic syntactic analyses, and these programs are generally based on a form of grammar, known as a context-free phrase structure (type 2) grammar.[9] Such grammars are characterized by the fact that the bracketing used to represent the sentence structure includes both juxtaposed bracket sets as well as nests of brackets, but that interleaving between different bracket pairs is not possible. For example, a structure such as

$$\{\{(A \cdot B) \cdot C\} \cdot [(D \cdot E) \cdot F \cdot \{G \cdot (H \cdot I)\}]\}$$

where the letters may stand for text words and the bracketing denotes phrase structure, could have been produced by a type 2 grammar. On the other hand, the structure

$$A \cdot \{(B \cdot C\} \cdot D)$$

is not producible by such a grammar, because of the interleaving between different bracket pairs.

Phrase structure analyses are of particular interest in the present context not only because a variety of machine programs exist which can perform such analyses automatically,[10] but also because phrase structure, as the name indicates, accounts for the most important word groupings, including noun phrases, prepositional phrases, adverbial phrases, and in most cases for the basic subject-verb-object grouping. These groups are also those which constitute the basic components to be identified in an automatic content analysis system. In the Syntol document processing system, for example, document content is represented by graphs in which each branch together with its adjacent nodes represents the equivalent of a phrase structure component.[4, 5, 6] The construction of a typical Syntol information graph is illustrated in Fig. 1.

Some phrases or word groups whose component words do not occur in adjacent word positions within a sentence are difficult to generate by an unmodified phrase structure grammar. This is the case notably of phrases with the so-called discontinuous constituents (for example, "call up" in

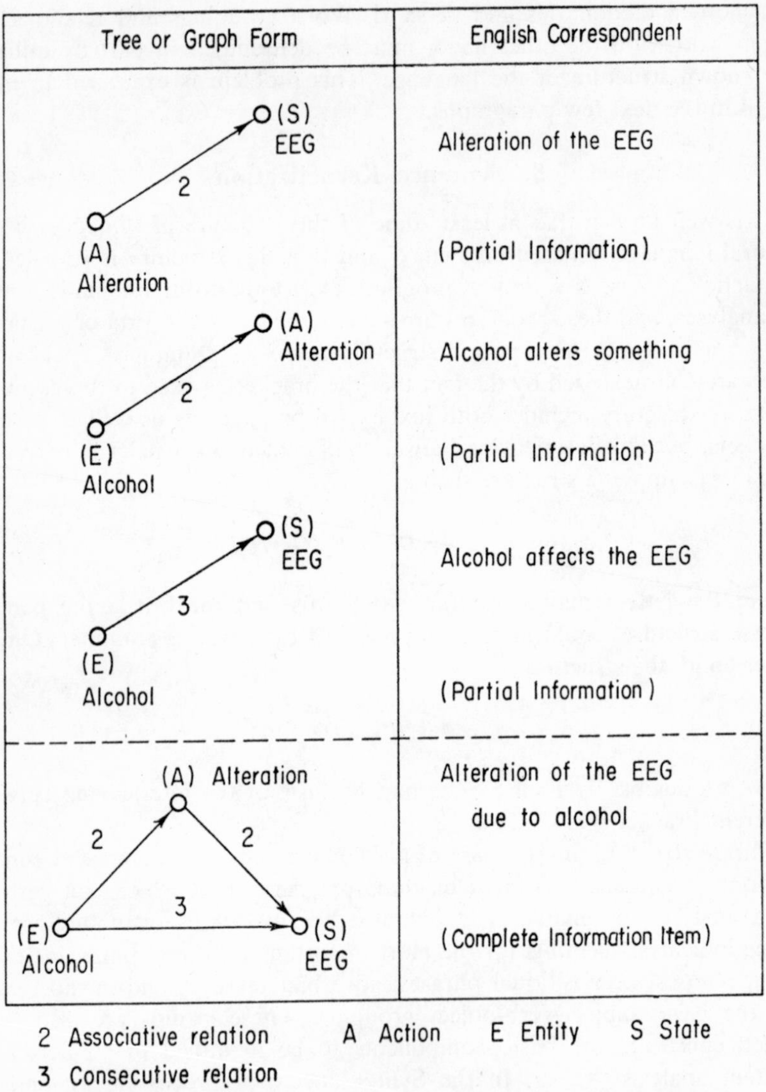
Tree or Graph Form
English Correspondent
(S)
EEG
2
(A)
Alteration
Alteration of the EEG
(Partial Information)
(A)
Alteration
2
(E)
Alcohol
Alcohol alters something
(Partial Information)
(S)
EEG
3
(E)
Alcohol
Alcohol affects the EEG
(Partial Information)
(A) Alteration
2
2
3
(E)
Alcohol
(S)
EEG
Alteration of the EEG
due to alcohol
(Complete Information Item)
2 Associative relation
3 Consecutive relation
A Action
E Entity
S State

Fig. 1. Construction of a typical Syntol information graph.

"call him up"). In order to accommodate discontinuous constituents, the normal type 2 production rules must be extended, thus tending to produce a relatively complicated grammar.[10, 11]

Some important linguistic phenomena do not fit into a phrase structure model, even if extended to handle special cases such as discontinuous constituents. There is no way in a phrase structure model to relate, for example, two semantically identical sentences of which one is in the passive and the other in the active voice. It is often suggested, therefore, that in order to produce correct word groupings for a variety of transformed structures, a transformational grammar be added to the phrase structure model. Such a move could be expected to produce not only a grammar more nearly representative of natural language structure as it exists, but would also result in a simpler, more economical, phrase structure component.

A possible procedure advocated for an automatic sentence analysis then consists of two main steps. First, the structural diversity of ordinary text is eliminated by using both a phrase structure and a transformational grammar component to produce for each sentence a set of standard, simple syntactic structures, known as *kernels*. Second, semantically equivalent kernels are identified. The kernelization process itself might be effected by an alternate application of phrase structure and transformational rules. Specifically, phrase structure rules are used first to produce a standard phrase structure analysis of an input string; the analyzed string is then subjected to all applicable inverse transformations. The transformed strings are then analyzed once more, and so on, until no further change is produced in the output.[12, 13] A sample sentence and the corresponding kernels produced by a typical kernelizing system are shown in Fig. 2.[14]

Give algorithms useful for the numerical solution of ordinary differential equations and partial differential equations on digital computers.

(a) Original Text

		Rule Number
1.	X gives algorithms.	*1
2.	Algorithms are useful.	*2
3.	for solution	F2
4.	Solution is numerical.	T2
5.	of equations	F2
6.	Equations are ordinary.	T2
7.	differential equations	F1
8.	Equations are partial.	T2
9.	differential equations	F1
10.	on computers	F2
11.	Computers are digital.	T2

(b) Corresponding Kernels

1. Kernel *fragments* are not followed by periods; kernel *sentences* are always followed by periods.

2. Indentation of kernel fragments or sentences denotes subordination to the sentence or fragment immediately preceding.

Fig. 2. Sentence kernelization.

Under the assumption that each kernel thus produced represents one of the word groups to be generated during a content analysis process, a kernelization procedure would seem to be both necessary and sufficient for an adequate automatic text processing system. Unfortunately, the apparatus required to use a transformational grammar as part of an automatic system may be expected to be much more complex than the simple pushdown store analysis, or list-tracing procedures, needed to use a simple phrase structure grammar. Furthermore, the problem as to what constitutes a sufficient kernel set is as yet unresolved, and most existing kernelizing systems are of an experimental nature and have not been subjected to extensive tests.[14, 15, 16]

Since many text processing systems, including in particular most document retrieval systems, require the identification of only the principal semantically equivalent structures, rather than of *all* meaningful word groupings obtainable from a text, a procedure which bypasses the complete kernelization in favor of a simpler one-step phrase recognition process, may be of considerable practical importance. Such a procedure is outlined in the next few sections after a brief description of the SMART automatic document retrieval system.

4. The SMART Retrieval System

The SMART retrieval system [17, 18] takes both documents and search requests in unrestricted English, performs a complete content analysis automatically, and retrieves those documents which most nearly match the given search request. A large variety of procedures are available for the generation of the content identifiers attached to both search requests and stored documents, and documents may therefore be retrieved in accordance with many different criteria.

The system can be controlled by the user in that a search request is first processed in a standard mode; the user is then asked to analyze the output obtained, and depending on his further requirements, the original search request can be reprocessed using a new processing method. The new output is then again examined and the process can be iterated until such time as the right kind and amount of information is retrieved. The various processing modes correspond to different automatic methods of analyzing information, and the iterative procedure represents an attempt to approximate, with natural language input, the type of analysis (in terms of controlled concepts together with controlled relations between them) previously illustrated by the semimanual process of Fig. 1. Before exhibiting the differences between the theoretically desirable and the actually achievable reduction, some of the basic SMART operations are outlined briefly.

The first operation consists generally in a *stem-suffix cut-off* operation, which replaces each text word occurring in a document or in a search request by the corresponding word stem. High-frequency function words, such as conjunctions, prepositions, and the like may then be temporarily discarded, and a document (or a search request) can be identified by the set of remaining word stems, together with a frequency indicator for each stem. At this point, the word stems used to represent item properties are not as yet normalized.

In order to reduce synonymous word stems to a single "concept," and to provide a variety of different concept identifications for the many stem homographs which may arise in the natural language, it is necessary to perform a *thesaurus look-up* operation. This process effectively replaces each word stem by one or more so-called concept numbers. The replacement of word stems by concept numbers is illustrated in Fig. 3 for a typical

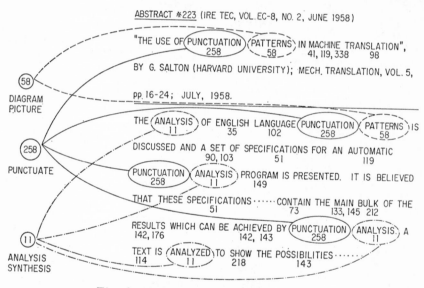

Fig. 3. Assignment of concept numbers.

document abstract included in SMART. Use of the thesaurus insures that a given document is identified by a set of controlled terms.

Generic relations between properties may be provided by consulting a *hierarchical arrangement* of concept numbers as shown in Fig. 4. Specifically, given any concept obtained from the thesaurus, it is now possible to obtain related concepts by using the tree structures. More general concepts may be located by going "up" in the tree, more specific ones by going "down," and various related concepts may be picked up by locating the

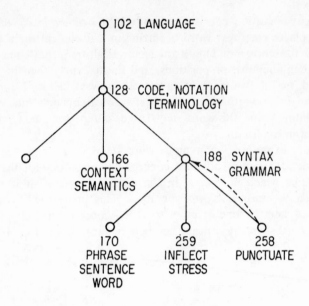

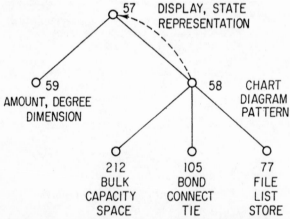

Fig. 4. Hierarchy excerpt showing expansion.

"brothers" (nodes in the same filial set) of a given concept. Fig. 4 illustrates, for example, the expansion of concept 258 (punctuation) into concept 188 (syntax), and of 58 (pattern) into 57 (representation).

Relations between concepts may be added by grouping the concepts instead of using them one at a time. The identification of so-called *statistical phrases* is illustrated in Fig. 5 for the document abstract previously shown in Fig. 3. Statistical phrases are groups of concepts which co-occur within the sentences of the documents with a frequency exceeding some pre-established threshold. If such a group of concepts is detected, the individual concept numbers may be replaced by a group concept number attached to the statistical phrase; such a phrase concept may then be given a higher weight than the individual word concepts when it is used as part of a document identification.

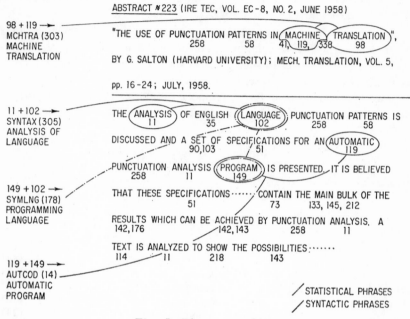

Fig. 5. Phrase matching.

In the abstract of Fig. 5, co-occurrence in the same sentence of concepts 11 (analysis) and 102 (language) is recognized as a phrase with concept number 305 (language analysis); similarly for concepts 102 (language) and 149 (program), which are transformed into 178 (programming language). The exact type of relation which obtains between a concept pair included in a given statistical phrase cannot in general be determined, since the formation of such phrases depends strictly on concept co-occurrence characteristics. Thus, the use of statistical phrases does not completely fill the requirements of the graph model of Fig. 1, where the principal relations are identified completely.

An attempt to identify at least some relations between concepts may be made by using the syntax of the language. Specifically, statistical phrases may be replaced by *syntactic phrases* in which the included concepts exhibit some specified syntactic relationship. In order to be able to include syntactic relationships as part of the content identification process, it is necessary to perform an automatic syntactic analysis. Such a step is included in the SMART system, and procedures are provided for eliminating statistical phrases which do not qualify as proper syntactic phrases. In the abstract of Fig. 5, for example, the statistical phrase corresponding to concept 178 (programming language) is not a syntactic phrase, since an admissible syntactic relation does not exist between the included concepts 102 (language) and 149 (program).

Identification of syntactic relationships between concepts included in a phrase does furnish some relational indications in accordance with the requirements of the model of Fig. 1. However, in order to generate a completely defined graph structure, both concepts and relations must be properly normalized. That is, different syntactic structures must be transformed into the same phrase if there exists semantic equivalence. A procedure to

Method of Generation	Identifiers		
	Concept Numbers	English Examples (Weights)	
	11	Analysis, Synthesis	(48)
	58	Diagram, Picture	(24)
	59	Amount, Extent	(12)
Thesaurus	98	Translation	(12)
Look-Up	102	Language	(12)
	119	Automatic, Machine	(24)
	149	Program, Routine	(12)
	170	Phrase, Word, Sentence	(12)
	258	Punctuation	(48)
	57 (58,59)	Display, Represent	(36)
Hierarchy	112 (119)	Manipulate, Operate	(24)
Expansion	188 (170,258)	Grammar, Syntax	(60)
Statistical	178 (149,102)	SYMLNG (program, language)	(36)
Phrases	305 (11,170)	SYNTAX (analysis, word)	(36)
	303 (119,98)	MCHTRA (machine translation)	(36)
Syntactic	305 (11,102)	SYNTAX (analysis of language)	(36)
Phrases	14 (119,149)	AUTCOD (automatic program)	(36)

Fig. 6. Identification of abstract number 223.

perform the required transformations is further described in the next few paragraphs.

The complete content analysis process is summarized in Fig. 6 for the document abstract previously shown in Figs. 3 and 5.

5. Syntactic Phrase Matching

The identification of information items by concept numbers and phrases of various kinds is of use only if the corresponding identifiers are, in fact, properly normalized. This is achieved in the SMART system by replacing words by concept numbers, by performing a syntactic analysis of the sentences occurring in documents and search requests so as to determine syntactic (phrase structure) relations between concepts, and finally by looking up the resulting syntactic structures in a dictionary of *criterion trees.*

Criterion trees consist of prestored frames including concept numbers, syntactic indicators, and the syntactic relations which obtain between the included concepts. There exist four main classes of criterion trees as shown in Fig. 7, corresponding to noun phrases, subject-verb relations, verb-object relations, and subject-object relations. The syntactic structure of criterion trees is conveniently specified by syntactic "dependency" trees as seen in the center section of Fig. 7.* The top-most tree in Fig. 7 corresponds, for example, to an English phrase consisting of an adjective (A), or noun (N), (tree node 2) which is syntactically dependent upon another noun specified by tree node 1.

The operations of the criterion tree dictionary may be explained by considering the example of Fig. 8. The tree, termed SYNTAX, is defined at the top of the figure. Node 1 of the tree must correspond to either concepts 11 or 158, and node 2 to concepts 102, 188, or 170. Furthermore, four different syntactic frames are allowed for the tree, as indicated by the format numbers which follow the $ sign (fourteen different formats are used at present in the criterion tree dictionary). A few typical word stems corresponding to the concepts included in the SYNTAX tree specification are also shown in Fig. 8, as are examples of English phrases and sentences which will match the given tree.

Obviously, the multiplicity of concepts attached to a given node of a criterion tree, and the variety of permissible syntactic formats guarantees that a given criterion tree specification corresponds to hundreds of different English constructions. Furthermore, both documents and search requests use the same criterion tree dictionary, so that a flexible matching process

---

* Dependency grammars are equivalent, for present purposes, with phrase structure grammars, and the respective tree representations may be used interchangeably.19

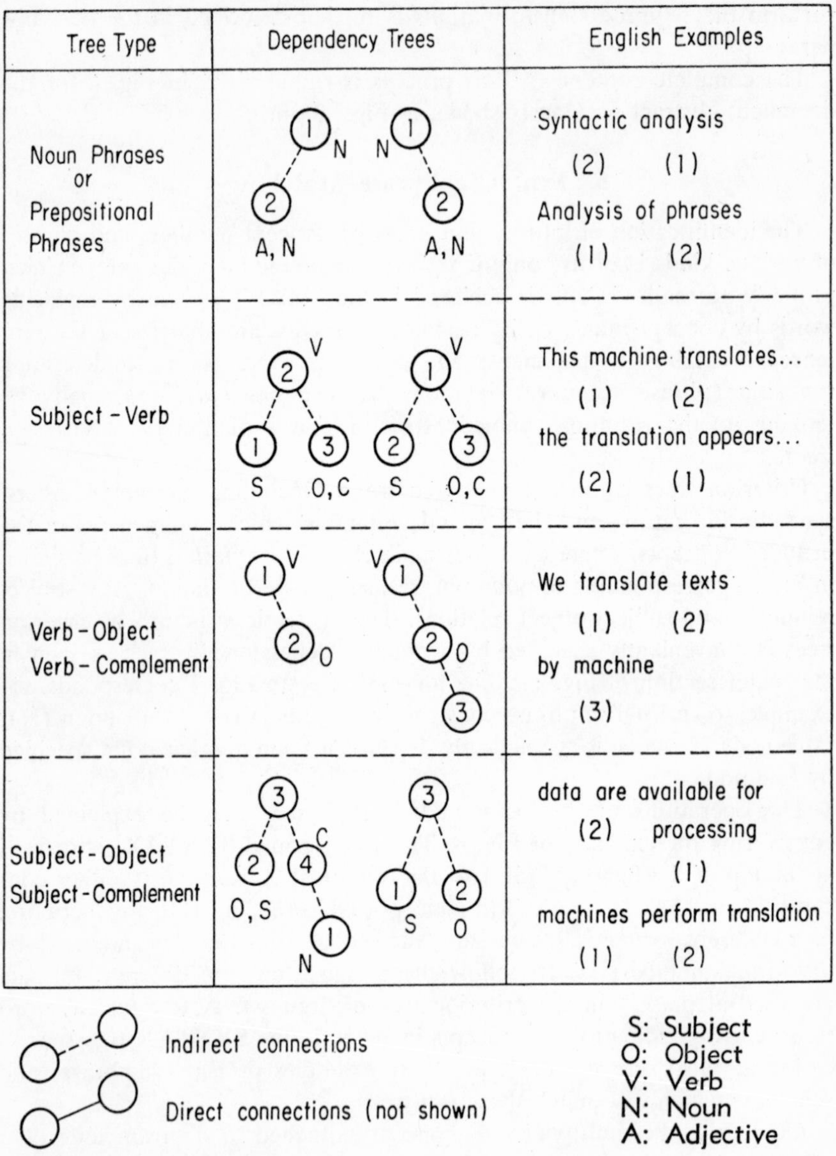

Tree Type	Dependency Trees	English Examples
Noun Phrases or Prepositional Phrases	(1) N N (1) / (2) A,N (2) A,N	Syntactic analysis (2) (1) Analysis of phrases (1) (2)
Subject – Verb	V (2) V (1) / (1) (3) (2) (3) S O,C S O,C	This machine translates... (1) (2) the translation appears... (2) (1)
Verb – Object Verb – Complement	(1) V V (1) (2) O (2) O (3)	We translate texts (1) (2) by machine (3)
Subject – Object Subject – Complement	(3) (3) (2) (4) C (1) (2) O,S (1) S O N	data are available for (2) processing (1) machines perform translation (1) (2)

Indirect connections

Direct connections (not shown)

S: Subject
O: Object
V: Verb
N: Noun
A: Adjective

Fig. 7. Basic criterion tree classes.

ensues. The comparison of concept numbers and of syntactic indicators is done in the SMART system by table look-up, and the dependency structures of input sentences and criterion trees are compared by an efficient graph-matching process.[20, 21] The Kuno-Oettinger multiple path syntactic analyzer is used to perform the automatic syntactic analysis of the input documents.*22

As an example, a typical search request processed through the SMART system is shown in Fig. 9. The output of the syntactic analysis of the first sentence of the request is given in Fig. 10. Finally, the criterion tree match-

PHRASE SPECIFICATION:

SYNTAX (11,158) / (102,188,170) $ 1,3,4,13

CONCEPT NODE 1   CONCEPT NODE 2   FORMATS

NODE 1	NODE 2	FORMATS	SAMPLE PHRASES
11 ANAL SYNTHESIS SYNTHES SYNTHET	102 INTERLINGU LANGUAGE	1 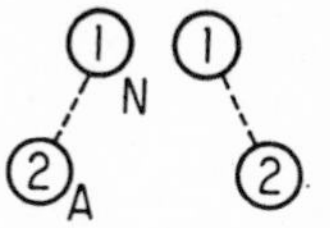	1 SYNTACTIC ANALYSIS PHRASE RELATIONS ANALYSIS OF SENTENCES
158 CLASS CORRESPOND GROUP INDEPEND	107 PHRASE SENTENCE SUBJECT WORD	3 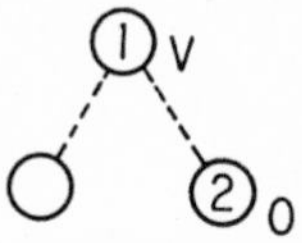	3 WE CAN ANALYZE THE LANGUAGE .....SYNTHESIZE A SYNTAX
		4 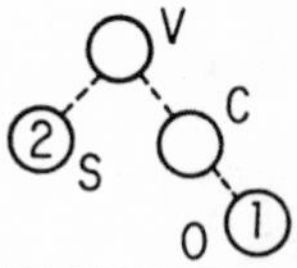	4 THE GRAMMAR IS NOW AVAILABLE FOR ANALYSIS
RELATE	188 GRAMMAR SYNTAX SYNTACTIC	13 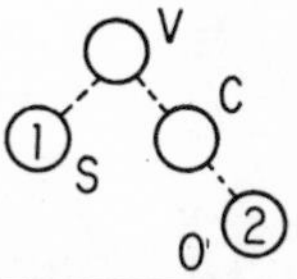	13 THE ANALYSIS IS APPLICABLE TO RUSSIAN GRAMMAR

Fig. 8. Criterion phrase specifications.

(For explanation of symbols, see Fig. 7)

ing procedure is illustrated in Fig. 11, where it is seen that sentence nodes 12 and 14 ("equations" and "differential") match tree number 47 in the criterion tree dictionary, while sentence nodes 9 and 7 match tree number 87. The concept numbers newly obtained as a result of the criterion tree matching process (concept 379 representing "differential equations," and

---

* It is obvious that if the syntactic analysis procedure furnishes an incorrect or a doubtful analysis, the phrase matching process may be affected adversely.

```
ENGLISH TEXT PROVIDED FOR DOCUMENT  DIFFERNTL EQ           SEPTEMBER 28, 1964    PAGE 345

    GIVE ALGORITHMS USEFUL FOR THE NUMERICAL SOLUTION OF ORDINARY DIFFER-      1
    ENTIAL EQUATIONS AND PARTIAL DIFFERENTIAL EQUATIONS ON DIGITAL             1
    COMPUTERS .  EVALUATE THE VARIOUS INTEGRATION PROCEDURES (TRY              1
    RUNGE-KUTTA, MILNE-S METHOD) WITH RESPECT TO ACCURACY, STABILITY, AND      2
    SPEED .                                                                    2


WORDS IN DOCUMENT DIFFERNTL EQ NOT FOUND IN THESAURUS      SEPTEMBER 28, 1964    PAGE 346

    WORD NOT FOUND     KIND    LOC. NUM        SENTENCE AND WORD NUMBERS

    RESPECT            STEM     8    1              2,  14
```

Fig. 9. Search Request "Differntl Eq" Processed by SMART System

```
SYNTACTIC ANALYSIS OF SENTENCES FROM TLXT DIFFERNTL EQ     SEPTFMBER 28, 1964    PAGE 348

***** ANALYSIS NUMBER      1                              OF SENTENCE NUMBER   000001

ENGLISH        SENTENCE STRUCTURE   SNC   SNC CODE           SYNTACTIC ROLE            RL NUM PREDICTION POOL

                                                                                        SE
GIVE           3V                   ITL   INFINITE VTI       IMPERATIVE VERB           SEITLO   PD N2B
ALGORITHMS     30                   NQUP  NOUN 1             OBJECT OF IMPERATIVE VERB N2NNN1   PD AP
USEFUL         30A                  ADJ   ADJECTIVE 1        POST-POSITIONAL ADJECTIVE APADJO   PD
FOR            30APK                PRE   PREPOSITION        PREPOSITION               PDPREO   PD NQG
THE            3OAPUA               ART   PRO-ADJECTIVE      OBJECT OF PREPOSITION     NQAAAO   PD NQG
NUMERICAL      3OAPUA               ADJ   ADJECTIVE 1        OBJECT OF PREPOSITION     N5ADJO   PD N5G
SOLUTION       30APO                NOUS  NOUN 1             OBJECT OF PREPOSITION     N5MMMO   PD N5G
OF             3OAPUPR              PRE   PREPOSITION        PREPOSITION               XDPRE1   PD NQGZDB
ORDINARY       3OAPOPUA             ADJ   ADJECTIVE 1        OBJECT OF PREPOSITION     NQAAAO   PD NQGXDBNQG
DIFFERENTIAL   3OAPUPUA             ADJ   ADJECTIVE 1        OBJECT OF PREPOSITION     N5ADJO   PD NQGXDBN5G
EQUATIONS      3OAPUPO              NQUP  NOUN 1             OBJECT OF PREPOSITION     N5MMMO   PD NQGXDBN5G
AND            3OAP+                XCO   COORDINATE CCNJ    COMPOUND OBJECT           XDXCDO   PD NQGXD8
PARTIAL        3OAPUA               ADJ   ADJECTIVE 1        OBJECT OF PREPOSITION     NQAAAO   PD NQG
DIFFERENTIAL   3OAPUA               ADJ   ADJECTIVE 1        OBJECT OF PREPOSITION     N5ADJO   PD N5G
EQUATIONS      3OAPU                NQUP  NOUN 1             OBJECT OF PREPOSITION     N5MMMO   PD N5G
ON             3OAPUPR              PRE   PREPOSITION        PREPOSITION               PDPREO   PD
DIGITAL        3OAPUUA              ADJ   ADJECTIVE 1        OBJECT OF PREPOSITION     NQAAAO   PD NQG
COMPUTERS      3OAPUU               NQUP  NOUN 1             OBJECT OF PREPOSITION     N5MMMO   PD N5G
.              3.                   PRD   PERIOD             END OF SENTENCE           PDPRDO   PD

POOL OVERFLOWS=   0  NUMBER TEST FAILURES=   0 SHAPER OVERFLOWS=   229 NESTER OVERFLOWS=   59 TIME=   0.0 MINUTES   1
```

Fig. 10. Syntactic Analysis of Sentence 1, DIFFERNTL EQ

THESE ARE THE TEXT, .NODE NUMBERS, AND STRINGS OF SENTENCE NO. OCOO01   SEPTEMBER 28, 1964   PAGE 347

```
GIVE                    2    3V
ALGORITHMS              3    30
USEFUL                  4    30A
FOR                     6    30APR
THE                     8    30APOA
NUMERICAL               9    30APOA
SOLUTION                7    30APO
OF                     11    30APOPR
ORDINARY               13    30APOPDA
DIFFERENTIAL           14    30APOPDOA
EQUATIONS              12    30APOPO
AND                     5    30AP+
PARTIAL                16    30APUA
DIFFERENTIAL           17    30APOA
EQUATIONS              15    30APO
ON                     19    30APOPR
DIGITAL                21    30APOPOA
COMPUTERS              20    30APOPO
```
SYNTACTIC
ANALYSIS
OUTPUT

NODE CORRESPONDENCES OF TREE WITH INDEX =DIFEQU, SERIAL NO.   47, AND OUTPUT CONCEPT NOS
```
TREE   SENTENCE
 1       12 - KEY
 2       14
```

NODE CORRESPONDENCES OF TREE WITH INDEX =NUMERI, SERIAL NO.   87, AND OUTPUT CONCEPT NOS
```
TREE   SENTENCE
 2        9
 1        7 - KEY
```
PHRASE
MATCHING

THE CRITERION ROUTINE HAS PROCESSED   1 SENTENCES, HAVING   2 MATCHES OF   2 DISTINCT INDICES.

TREES DETECTED SYNTACTICALLY IN DOCUMENT DIFFERNTL EQ

```
TREE   CONCEPT   OCCURRED   COMPONENT CONCEPTS

DIFEQU  379DIF      1        274DIF 181QUA
NUMERI  375NUM      1         13CALC 11ALYS
```
SYNTACTIC
TREE
OUTPUT

Fig. 11. Syntactic Phrase Matching

concept 375 representing "numerical analysis") are shown at the bottom of Fig. 11.

6. Evaluation of the Phrase-Matching Process

In order to evaluate to what extent the automatic criterion tree procedures can approximate the manual analysis specified by the model of Fig. 1, it is of interest to examine in more detail the variety of different structures which can be matched. The flexibility of the procedure arises from four principal characteristics of the criterion trees:

1. Word stems rather than complete words are used during the thesaurus look-up.
2. Concept numbers rather than words or word stems are attached to the criterion tree nodes.
3. Each criterion tree is assigned several possible syntactic frames, or equivalently, a variety of syntactic relations are normally allowed betwen concepts.
4. The dependency connection between two specified concept numbers is an *indirect* connection, ignoring occurrences of extraneous concepts, or of function words which may be part of the syntactic context (thus, the preposition "of" in the phrase "retrieval of information" is ignored when the dependency trees are matched).*

As a result of this type of criterion tree specification, it is in general possible to match semantically equivalent phrases or sentences, provided that the same basic order between major sentence parts (subject, verb, object) is present. Differences due to addition or deletion of auxiliary particles and phrases, shifts from noun to verb constructions or vice-versa, use of synonyms and of multiple subjects, verbs, or objects do not in general interfere with the matching procedure. Examples of various syntactic constructions which can be properly recognized by the criterion tree procedure are given in Fig. 12.† Within each group, each set of sample phrases matches the same basic criterion tree.

Since function words, including prepositions, adverbs, and conjunctions, are not normally included in a criterion tree specification, a variety of structures which are not completely synonymous are nevertheless assumed to be identical by the criterion tree routine. Typical examples of the non-recognition of semantic differences, as well as some examples of the non-recognition of semantic similarities are shown in Fig. 13. Fig. 13 may in fact be considered to be a repertoire of the deficiencies of the SMART

---

* This feature is also incorporated in a somewhat different form in a number of other text processing systems.[23]

† Some of the examples included in Figs. 12 and 13 were suggested in studies dealing with the construction of transformational grammars.[24, 25]

Transformations Correctly Identified	Examples of Matching Structures
1. declarative v. interrogative (word order between principal sentence parts is maintained)	the *man bats* the *ball* does the *man bat* the *ball* the boy asks whether the *man bats* the *ball*
2. identification of multiple subjects, verbs, objects	the large, grey, empty hall . . . the large hall . . . the grey hall . . .
3. "there is" or "it is" constructions	the car is in the garage there is a car in the garage
4. deletions of certain pronouns	this is the information that you wanted this is the information you wanted
5. permutations within noun and prepositional phrases	pattern analysis . . . the analysis of patterns . . .
6. some negative constructions	children do not like teachers no children like teachers
7. identification of synonymous constructions	the grammar of this coding system . . . the syntax of this notation . . .
8. identification of stem similarities	analyzer . . . analysis . . .
9. verb-noun shifts	he dances; he is a dancer he looks; he gives a look
10. addition of subject or object clauses	the boy works the father demands that the boy should work
11. certain equivalent constructions	how much . . .; what . . . which time . . .; at what time . . . for more than . . .; for longer than . . .

Fig. 12. Correctly identified phrase and sentence transformations.

phrase matching process. The nonrecognition of the semantic differences illustrated in examples 2, 3, and 7 of Fig. 13 is generally of no consequence for document retrieval, and may also be of relatively minor importance in question-answering systems. On the other hand, the nonrecognition of some of the semantic similarities, notably those illustrated by examples 1 and 5, may be expected to be serious, at least for automatic question-answering.

To summarize, in many text processing systems, semantically equivalent expressions may be recognized without complete kernelization of all sentences, by matching syntactically analyzed texts against a dictionary of syntactic frames (criterion trees) furnished with suitable syntactic markers

Type of Deficiency	Examples {matching} ≠ not matching ≠
1. active-passive changes not immediately identified (due to change in basic structure)	the man hits the ball ≠ the ball is hit by the man ≠ ("man eats dog," "dog eats man" are, however, distinguished)
2. no distinction between depth of dependency connection	{ analysis of English patterns / analysis of English / analysis of patterns }
3. no recognition of negative-positive transformation	{ the sun shines / the sun does not shine }
4. no recognition of some relative clauses causing word order changes	I saw the man ≠ It is he whom I saw ≠
5. no recognition of dependencies across sentence boundaries	Mr. X is tall. He is our teacher. ≠ Mr. X is our teacher. ≠
6. no recognition of unstated classifications	This poodle is big ≠ This poodle is a big dog ≠ They are 1,000 feet apart ≠ The distance between them is 1,000 feet. ≠
7. no recognition of distinct verb forms	{ The data are retrieved / The data were retrieved / The data have not been retrieved }

{ nonrecognition of semantic differences
≠ nonrecognition of semantic similarities

Fig. 13. Deficiencies in phrase matching process.

and semantic labels. This process recognizes, in particular, transformations involving the principal phrase structure components, including noun phrases, prepositional phrases, and subject-verb-object groupings. Additional transformed structures, such as those depending on function words which are not now taken into account, could be recognized at the cost of complicating the criterion tree specification. The presently operating criterion tree routine is suitable for automatic analysis of document content; for unrestricted question-answering systems, where a complete semantic recognition may be required, the criterion tree method may still be used as a first step, to simplify a more complete kernelizing routine to follow.

References

1. H. P. Luhn, "A Statistical Approach to Mechanized Encoding and Searching of Literary Information," *IBM Journal of Research and Development*, Vol. 1, No. 4 (October 1957).

2. J. J. Robinson, "Preliminary Codes and Rules for the Automatic Parsing of English," *Rand Memorandum RM-3339-PR*, RAND Corporation (December 1963).

3. J. J. Robinson, "Automatic Parsing and Fact Retrieval: A Comment on Grammar, Paraphrase, and Meaning," *Rand Memorandum RM-4005-PR*, RAND Corporation (February 1964).

4. J. C. Gardin and F. Levy, "Le Syntol-Syntagmatic Organization Language," *Proceedings IFIP Congress-62*, North Holland Publishing Company (1962).

5. J. C. Gardin, *et al.*, "Final Report on a General System for the Treatment of Documentary Data (Theoretical Applications of Syntol—Part I, Programming of Syntol—Part II)," Association Marc Bloch (October 1963).

6. M. Coyaud, "Analyse Automatique Syntol," presented at the NATO Advanced Study Institute on Automatic Documentation, Venice (July 1963).

7. F. Black, "A Deductive Question-Answering System," Doctoral Thesis, Harvard University (June 1964).

8. W. S. Cooper, "Fact Retrieval and Deductive Question-Answering Information Retrieval Systems," *Journal of the ACM*, Vol. 11, No. 2 (April 1964).

9. N. Chomsky, *Syntactic Structures*, Mouton, s'Gravenhage (1957).

10. D. G. Bobrow, "Syntactic Analysis of English by Computer—A Survey," *Proceedings AFIPS Fall Joint Computer Conference*, Vol. 24, Las Vegas (1963).

11. V. H. Yngve, "Computer Programs for Translation," *Scientific American* (June 1962).

12. S. R. Petrick, "A Recognition Procedure for Transformational Grammars," *Proceedings of the 2nd Congress in the Information System Sciences*, Hot Springs (November 1964).

13. H. G. Herzberger, "Some Aspects of Kernelization," Western Reserve University (November 1963).

14. D. Foster, "Automatic Sentence Kernelization," Seminar Paper written in Applied Mathematics 205, Harvard University, Spring 1964.

15. B. T. Carmody, and P. E. Jones, Jr., "Automatic Derivation of Constituent Sentences," *1964 Annual Meeting of the Association for Machine Translation and Computational Linguistics*, Indiana University (1964).

16. D. G. Bobrow, "Natural Language Input for a Computer Problem-Solving System," *MIT Report MAC-TR-1* (September 1964).

17. G. Salton *et al.*, *Information Storage and Retrieval*, Reports No. ISR-7 and 8 to the National Science Foundation, Computation Laboratory of Harvard University (June and December 1964).

18. G. Salton, "A Document Retrieval System for Man-Machine Interaction," *Proceedings of the ACM 19th National Conference*, Philadelphia (1964).

19. D. G. Hays, "Dependency Theory: A Formalism and Source Observations," *Rand Memorandum* RM-4087-PR, The RAND Corporation (July 1964).

20. E. H. Sussenguth, Jr., "Structure Matching in Information Processing," Doctoral Thesis, *Information Storage and Retrieval*, Report No. ISR-6 to the National Science Foundation, Computation Laboratory of Harvard University (April 1964).

21. G. Salton and E. H. Sussenguth, Jr., "Some Flexible Information Retrieval Systems Using Structure Matching Procedures," *Proceedings of the AFIPS Spring Joint Computer Conference*, Washington (April 1964).

22. S. Kuno and A. G. Oettinger, "Multiple-Path Syntactic Analyzer," *Proceedings IFIP Congress-62*, North Holland Publishing Company (1962).

23. S. Klein and R. F. Simmons, "Syntactic Dependency and the Computer Generation of Coherent Discourse," *Mechanical Translation*, Vol. 7, No. 2 (August 1963).

24. Z. S. Harris, "English Transformation List," Transform and Discourse Analysis Project, Paper No. 30, University of Pennsylvania (1964).

25. B. Hall, "Notes on Transformational Grammars," unpublished manuscript.

13 A Framework for Syntactic Translation

Victor H. Yngve

1. Introduction

The current M.I.T. approach to mechanical translation is aimed at providing routines intrinsically capable of producing correct and accurate translation. We are attempting to go beyond simple word-for-word translation; beyond translation using empirical, *ad hoc*, or pragmatic syntactic routines. The concept of full syntactic translation has emerged: translation based on a thorough understanding of linguistic structures, their equivalences, and meanings.

2. The Problems

The difficulties associated with word-for-word translation were appreciated from the very beginning, at least in outline form. Warren Weaver [1] and Erwin Reifler [2] in early memoranda called attention to the problems of multiple meaning, while Oswald and Fletcher [3] began by fixing their attention on the word-order problems—particularly glaring in the case of German-to-English word-for-word translations. Over the years it has become increasingly clear that most, if not all, of the problems associated with word-for-word translation can be solved by the proper manipulation or utilization of the context. Context is to be understood here in its broadest interpretation. Contextual clues were treated in detail in an earlier article.[4] The six types of clues discussed there will be reformulated briefly here. They are

1. The field of discourse. This was one of the earliest types of clues to be recognized. It can, by the use of specialized dictionaries, assist in the

Note: This work was performed at the Massachusetts Institute of Technology with the support of the U.S. Army (Signal Corps), The U.S. Air Force (Office of Scientific Research, Air Research and Development Command), and the U.S. Navy (Office of Naval Research); and with the support of the National Science Foundation. Reprinted from *Mechanical Translation*, Vol. 4, No. 3 (December 1957), pp. 59–65, with the permission of author and publisher.

189

selection of the proper meaning of words that carry different meanings in different fields of discourse. The field of discourse may be determined by the operator, who places the appropriate glossary in the machine; or it may be determined by a machine routine on the basis of the occurrences of certain text words that are diagnostic of the field.

2. Recognition of coherent word groups, such as idioms and compound nouns. This clue can provide a basis for translating such word groups correctly even when their meaning does not follow simply from the meanings of the separate words.

3. The syntactic function of each word. If the translating program can determine syntactic function, clues will be available for solving word-order problems as well as a large number of difficult multiple-meaning problems. Clues of this type will help, for example, in determining whether *der* in German should be translated as an article or as a relative or demonstrative pronoun, and whether it is nominative, genitive, or dative. They will also assist in handling the very difficult problems of translating prepositions correctly.

4. The selectional relations between words in open classes, that is, nouns, verbs, adjectives, and adverbs. These relations can be utilized by assigning the words to various meaning categories in such a way that when two or more of these words occur in certain syntactic relationships in the text, the correct meanings can be selected.

5. Antecedents. The ability of the translating program to determine antecedents will not only make possible the correct translation of pronouns, but will also materially assist in the translation of nouns and other words that refer to things previously mentioned.

6. All other contextual clues, especially those concerned with an exact knowledge of the subject under discussion. These will undoubtedly remain the last to be mechanized.

Finding out how to use these clues to provide correct and accurate translations by machine presents perhaps the most formidable task that language scholars have ever faced.

3. Two Approaches

Attempts to learn how to utilize the above-mentioned clues have followed two separate approaches. One will be called the "95 percent approach" because it attempts to find a number of relatively simple rules of thumb, each of which will translate a word or class of words correctly about 95 percent of the time, even though these rules are not based on a complete understanding of the problem. This approach is used by those who are seeking a short-cut to useful, if not completely adequate, translations. The other approach concentrates on trying to obtain a complete understanding of each portion of the problem so that completely adequate routines can be developed.

At any stage in the development of mechanical translation there will be some things that are perfectly understood and can therefore serve as the basis for perfect translation. In the area of verb, noun, and adjective inflection, it is possible to do a "100 percent job" because all the paradigms are available and all of the exceptions are known and have been listed. In this area one need not be satisfied with anything less than a perfect job.

At the same time there will be some things about language and translation that are not understood. It is in this area that the difference between the two approaches shows up. The question of when to translate the various German, French, or Russian verb categories into the different sets of English verb categories is imperfectly understood. Those who adopt the 95 percent approach will seek simple partial solutions that are right a substantial portion of the time. They gain the opportunity of showing early test results on a computer. Those who adopt the 100 percent approach realize that in the end satisfactory mechanical translation can follow only from the systematic enlarging of the area in which we have essentially perfect understanding.

The M. I. T. group has traditionally concentrated on moving segments of the problem out of the area where only the 95 percent approach is possible into the area where a 100 percent approach can be used. Looking at mechanical translation in this light poses the greater intellectual challenge, and we believe that it is here that the most significant advances can be made.

4. Syntactic Translation

Examination of the six types of clues mentioned above reveals that they are predominantly concerned with the relationships of one word to another in patterns. The third type—the ability of the program to determine the syntactic function of each word—is basic to the others. It is basic to the first: If the machine is to determine correctly the field of discourse at every point in the text, even when the field changes within one sentence, it must use the relationship of the words in syntactic patterns as the key for finding which words refer to which field. It is basic to the second because idioms, noun compounds, and so on, are merely special patterns of words that stand out from more regular patterns. It is basic to the fourth because here we are dealing with selectional relationships between words that are syntactically related. It is basic to the fifth because the relationship of a word to its antecedent is essentially a syntactic relationship. It is probably even basic to the last, the category of all other contextual clues.

Any approach to mechanical translation that attempts to go beyond mere word-for-word translation can with some justification be called a syntactic approach. The word "syntactic" can be used, however, to cover a number of different approaches. Following an early suggestion by Warren Weaver,[1] some of these take into consideration only the two or three immediately preceding and following words. Some of them, following a suggestion by Bar-Hillel,[5] do consider larger context, but by a complicated scanning forth and back in the sentence, looking for particular words or particular diacritics that have been attached to words in the first dictionary look-up. To the extent that these approaches operate without an accurate knowledge and use of the syntactic patterns of the languages, they are following the 95 percent approach.

Oswald and Fletcher [3] saw clearly that a solution to the word-order problems in German-to-English translation required the identification of syntactic units in the sentence, such as nominal blocks and verbal blocks. Recently, Brandwood [6] has extended and elaborated the rules of Oswald and Fletcher. Reifler,[7] too, has placed emphasis on form classes and the relationship of words one with the other. These last three attempts seem to come closer to the 100 percent way of looking at things.

Bar-Hillel,[8] at M. I. T., introduced a 100 percent approach years ago when he attempted to adapt to mechanical translation certain ideas of the Polish logician Ajdukiewicz. The algebraic notation adopted for syntactic categories, however, was not elaborate enough to express the relations of natural languages.

Later, the author [9, 10] proposed a syntactic method for solving multiple-meaning and word-order problems. This routine analyzed and translated the input sentences in terms of successively included clauses, phrases, and so forth.

More recently, Moloshnaya[11] has done some excellent work on English syntax, and Zarechnak[12] and Pyne[13] have been exploring with Russian a suggestion by Harris[14] that the text be broken down by transformations into kernel sentences which would be separately translated and then transformed back into full sentences. Lehmann,[15] too, has recently emphasized that translation of the German noun phrase into English will require a full descriptive analysis.

In much of the work there has been an explicit or implicit restriction to syntactic relationships that are contained entirely within a clause or sentence, although it is usually recognized that structural features, to a significant extent, cross sentence boundaries. In what follows, we will speak of the sentence without implying this restriction.

5. The Framework

The framework within which we are working is presented in schematic form in Fig. 1. This framework has evolved after careful consideration of a number of factors. Foremost among these is the necessity of breaking down a problem as complex as that of mechanical translation into a number of problems each of which is small enough to be handled by one person.

Fig. 1 represents a hypothetical translating machine. German sentences are fed in at the left. The recognition routine R.R. by referring to the grammar of German G_1 analyzes the German sentence and determines its structural description or specifier S_1 which contains all of the information that is in the input sentence. The part of the information that is implicit in the sentence (tense, voice, and so forth) is made explicit in S_1. Since a

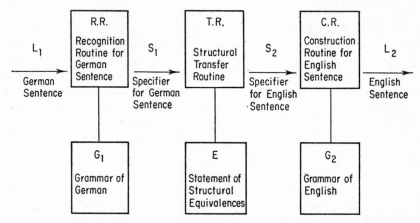

Fig. 1. A framework for mechanical translation.

German sentence and its English translation generally do not have identical structural descriptions, we need a statement of the equivalences E between English and German structures, and a structure transfer routine T.R. which consults E and transfers S_1 into S_2, the structural description, or specifier, of the English sentence. The construction routine C.R. is the routine that takes S_2 and constructs the appropriate English sentence in conformity with the grammar of English G_2.

This framework is similar to the one previously published[16] except that now we have added the center boxes and have a much better understanding of what was called the "message" or transition language—here, the specifiers. Andreyev [17] has also recently pointed out that translation is essentially a three-step process and that current published proposals have combined the first two steps into one. One might add that some of the published proposals even try to combine all three steps into one. The question of whether there are more than three steps will be taken up later.

A few simple considerations will make clear why it is necessary to describe the structure of each language separately. First, consider the regularities and irregularities of declensions and conjugations. These are, of course, entirely relative to one language.

Context, too, is by nature contained entirely within the framework of one language. In considering the translation of a certain German verb form into English, it is necessary to understand the German verb form as part of a complex of features of German structure including possibly other verb forms within the clause, certain adverbs, the structure of neighboring clauses, and the like. In translating into English, the appropriate complex of features relative to English structure must be provided so that each verb form is understood correctly as a part of that English complex.

The form of an English pronoun depends on its English antecedent, while the form of a German pronoun depends on its German antecedent—not always the same word because of the multiple-meaning situation. As important as it is to locate the antecedent of the input pronoun in the input text, it is equally important to embed the output pronoun in a proper context in the output language so that its antecedent is clear to the reader.

In all of these examples it is necessary to understand the complete system in order to program a machine to recognize the complex of features and to translate as well as a human translator. If one is not able to fathom the complete system, one has to fall back on hit-or-miss alternative methods— the 95 percent approach. In order to achieve the advantages of full syntactic translation, we will have to do much more very careful and detailed linguistic investigation.

6. Stored Knowledge

The diagram (Fig. 1) makes a distinction between the stored knowledge (the lower boxes) and the routines (the upper boxes). This distinction represents a point of view which may be academic: in an actual translating program the routine boxes and the stored knowledge boxes might be indistinguishable. For our purpose, however, the lower boxes represent our knowledge of the language and are intended not to include any details of the programming or, more particularly, any details of how the information about the languages is used by the machine. In other words, these boxes represent in an abstract fashion our understanding of the structures of the languages and of the translation equivalences. In an actual translating machine, the contents of these boxes will have to be expressed in some appropriate manner, and this might very well take the form of a program written in a pseudo code, programmable on a general-purpose computer. Earlier estimates 9 that the amount of storage necessary for syntactic information may be of the same order of magnitude as the amount of storage required for a dictionary have not been revised.

7. Construction

The Construction Routine C.R. in Fig. 1, constructs to order an English sentence on the prescription of the specifier S_2. It does this by consulting its pharmacopoeia, the grammar of English G_2 which tells it how to mix the ingredients to obtain a correct and grammatical English sentence, the one prescribed.

The construction routine is a computer program that operates as a code conversion device, converting the code for the sentence, the specifier, into the English spelling of the sentence. The grammar may be looked upon in this light as a code book, or, more properly, as an algorithm for code conversion. Alternately, the construction routine can be regarded as a function generator. The independent variable is the specifier, and the calculated function is the output sentence. Under these circumstances, the grammar G_2 represents our knowledge of how to calculate the function.

The sentence construction routine resembles to some extent the very suggestive sentence generation concept of Chomsky,[18] but there is an important difference. Where sentence generation is concerned with a compact representation of the sentences of a language, sentence construction is concerned with constructing, to order, specified sentences one at a time. This difference in purpose necessitates far-reaching differences in the form of the grammars.

8. Specifiers

For an input to the sentence construction routine, we postulated an encoding of the information in the form of what we called a specifier. The specifier of a sentence represents that sentence as a series of choices within the limited range of choices prescribed by the grammar of the language. These choices are in the nature of values for the natural coordinates of the sentence in that language. For example: to specify an English sentence, one may have to specify for the finite verb first, second, or third person, singular or plural, present or past, whether the sentence is negative or affirmative, whether the subject is modified by a relative clause, and which one, and so on. The specifier also specifies the class to which the verb belongs, and ultimately, which verb of that class is to be used, and so on, through all of the details that are necessary to direct the construction routine to construct the particular sentence that satisfies the specifications laid down by the author of the original input sentence.

The natural coordinates of a language are not given to us a priori, they have to be discovered by linguistic research.

Ambiguity within a language can be looked at as unspecified coordinates.

A writer generally can be as unambiguous as he pleases—or as ambiguous. He can be less ambiguous merely by expanding on his thoughts, thus specifying the values of more coordinates. But there is a natural limit to how ambiguous he can be without circumlocutions. Ambiguity is a property of the particular language he is using in the sense that in each language certain types of ambiguity are not allowed in certain situations. In Chinese, one can be ambiguous about the tense of verbs, but in English this is not allowed: one must regularly specify present or past for verbs. On the other hand, one is usually ambiguous about the tense of adjectives in English, but in Japanese this is not allowed.

It may be worth while to distinguish between structural coordinates in the narrow sense and srtructural coordinates in a broader, perhaps extra-linguistic sense, that is, coordinates which might be called logical or mean-ing coordinates. As examples, one can cite certain English verb categories: in a narrow sense, the auxiliary verb "can" has two forms, present and past. This verb, however, cannot be made future or perfect as most other verbs can. One does not say "He has can come," but says, instead, "He has been able to come," which is structurally very different. It is a form of the verb "to be" followed by an adjective which takes the infinitive with "to." Again the auxiliary "must" has no past tense and again one uses a circumlocution—"had to." If we want to indicate the connection in mean-ing (paralleling a similarity in distribution) between "can" and "is able to" and between "must" and "has to," we have to use coordinates that are not structural in the narrow sense. As another example, there is the use of the present tense in English for past time (in narratives), for future time ("He is coming soon"), and with other meanings. Other examples, some bordering on stylistics, can also be cited to help establish the exis-tence of at least two kinds of sentence coordinates in a language, necessitat-ing at least two types of specifiers.

A translation routine that takes into consideration two types of specifiers for each language would constitute a five-step translation procedure. The incoming sentence would be analyzed in terms of a narrow structural speci-fier. This specifier would be converted into a more convenient and perhaps more meaningful broad specifier, which would then be converted into a broad specifier in the other language, then would follow the steps of con-version to a narrow specifier and to an output sentence.

9. Recognition

One needs to know what there is to be recognized before one can recog-nize it. Many people, including the author, have worked on recognition routines. Unfortunately, none of the work has been done with the necessary full and explicit knowledge of the linguistic structures and of the natural coordinates.

The question of how we understand a sentence is a valid one for linguists, and it may have an answer different from the answer to the question of how we produce a sentence. But it appears that the description of a language is more easily couched in terms of synthesis of sentences than in terms of analysis of sentences. The reason is clear. A description in terms of synthesis is straightforward and unambiguous. It is a one-to-one mapping of specifiers into sentences. But a description in terms of analysis runs into all of the ambiguities of language that are caused by the chance overlapping of different patterns: a given sentence may be understandable in terms of two or more different specifiers. Descriptions in terms of analysis will probably not be available until after we have the more easily obtained descriptions in terms of synthesis.

The details of the recognition routine will depend on the details of the structural description of the input language. Once this is available, the recognition routine itself should be quite straightforward. The method suggested earlier by the author 9 required that words be classified into word classes, phrases into phrase classes, and so on, on the basis of an adequate descriptive analysis. It operated by looking up word-class sequences, phrase-class sequences, and so on in a dictionary of allowed sequences.

10. Transfer of Structure

Different languages have different sets of natural coordinates. Thus the center boxes (Fig. 1) are needed to convert the specifiers for the sentences of the input language into the specifiers for the equivalent sentences in the output language. The real compromises in translation reside in these center boxes. It is here that the difficult and perhaps often impossible matching of sentences in different languages is undertaken. But the problems associated with the center box are not peculiar to mechanical translation. Human translators also face the very same problems when they attempt to translate. The only difference is that at present the human translators are able to cope satisfactorily with the problem.

We have presented a framework within which work can proceed that will eventually culminate in mechanical routines for full syntactic translation. There are many aspects of the problem that are not yet understood and many details remain to be worked out. We need detailed information concerning the natural coordinates of the languages. In order to transfer German specifiers into English specifiers, we must know something about these specifiers. Some very interesting comparative linguistic problems will undoubtedly turn up in this area.

The author wishes to express his indebtedness to his colleagues G. H. Matthews, Joseph Applegate, and Noam Chomsky, for some of the ideas expressed in this paper.

References

1. Warren Weaver, "Translation," *Machine Translation of Languages,* ed. William N. Locke and A. Donald Booth, Wiley, New York and London (1955).

2. Erwin Reifler, "Studies in Mechanical Translation No. 1, MT," mimeographed (January 1950).

3. Victor A. Oswald, Jr., and Stuart L. Fletcher, Jr., "Proposals for the Mechanical Resolution of German Syntax Patterns," *Modern Language Forum,* Vol. XXXVI, No. 2–4 (1951).

4. V. H. Yngve, "Terminology in the Light of Research on Mechanical Translation," *Babel,* Vol. 2, No. 3 (October 1956).

5. Y. Bar-Hillel, "The Present State of Research on Mechanical Translation," *American Documentation,* Vol. 2, pp. 229–237 (1951).

6. A. D. Booth, L. Brandwood, and J. P. Cleave, *Mechanical Resolution of Linguistic Problems,* Academic Press, New York (1958).

7. Erwin Reifler, "The Mechanical Determination of Meaning," *Machine Translation of Languages,* ed. William N. Locke and A. Donald Booth, Wiley, New York and London, 1955.

8. Y. Bar-Hillel, "A Quasi-Arithmetical Notation for Syntactic Description," *Language,* Vol. 29, No. 1 (1953).

9. V. H. Yngve, "Syntax and the Problem of Multiple Meaning," *Machine Translation of Languages,* ed. William N. Locke and A. Donald Booth, Wiley, New York and London, 1955.

10. V. H. Yngve, "The Technical Feasibility of Translating Languages by Machine," *Electrical Engineering,* Vol. 75, No. 11 (1956).

11. T. N. Moloshnaya, "Certain Questions of Syntax in Connection with Machine Translation from English to Russian," *Voprosy Yazykoznaniya,* No. 4 (1957).

12. M. M. Zarechnak, "Types of Russian Sentences," *Report of the Eighth Annual Round Table Meeting on Linguistics and Language Studies,* Georgetown University (1957).

13. J. A. Pyne, "Some Ideas on Inter-Structural Syntax," *Report of the Eighth Annual Round Table Meeting on Linguistics and Language Studies.* Georgetown University (1957).

14. Z. S. Harris, "Transfer Grammar," *International Journal of American Linguistics,* Vol. XX, No. 4 (October 1954).

15. W. P. Lehmann, "Structure of Noun Phrases in German," *Report of the Eighth Annual Round Table Meeting on Linguistics and Language Studies.* Georgetown University (1957).

16. V. H. Yngve, "Sentence-for-Sentence Translation," *Mechanical Translation,* Vol. 2, No. 2 (1955).

17. N. D. Andreyev, "Machine Translation and the Problem of an Intermediary Language, *Voprosy Yazykoznaniya,* No. 5 (1957).

18. Noam Chomsky, *Syntactic Structures,* Mouton, The Hague (1957).

Index